THE BIG BOOK OF LOOK & LOOK AGAIN

Kidsbooks®

Visit us at www.kidsbooks.com®

Strange-But-True Mysteries

THE GIANT STATUES OF EASTER ISLAND

On Easter Sunday in 1722, Dutch Admiral Jacob Roggeveen sailed to a small island in the South Pacific. When he went ashore, he discovered more than 600 giant statues carved from stone, some of which were over 40 feet tall. In 1947, Thor Heyerdahl, a Norwegian archaeologist, led an expedition to try to find out how the statues got there.

LEARN ABOUT THE GIANT STATUES OF EASTER ISLAND
AS YOU LOOK FOR THESE FUN ITEMS:

- ☐ Artist
- ☐ Banana leaves
- ☐ Bone
- ☐ Carrot
- ☐ Drum
- ☐ Duck
- ☐ Flower
- ☐ Flying bat
- ☐ Football
- ☐ Graduate
- ☐ Guitar
- ☑ Key
- ☐ Ladder
- ☐ Mouse
- ☐ Owl
- ☐ Painted eggs (3)
- ☐ Party hats (2)
- ☐ Pelican
- ☐ Periscope
- ☐ Photographer
- ☐ Ring
- ☐ Rocking chair
- ☐ Skateboard
- ☐ Stars (3)
- ☐ Telescope
- ☐ Toucan
- ☐ Truck
- ☐ Unicorn
- ☐ Wagon
- ☐ Water bucket
- ☐ Witch

What was used to carve the statues? What was the name of Thor Heyerdahl's craft?

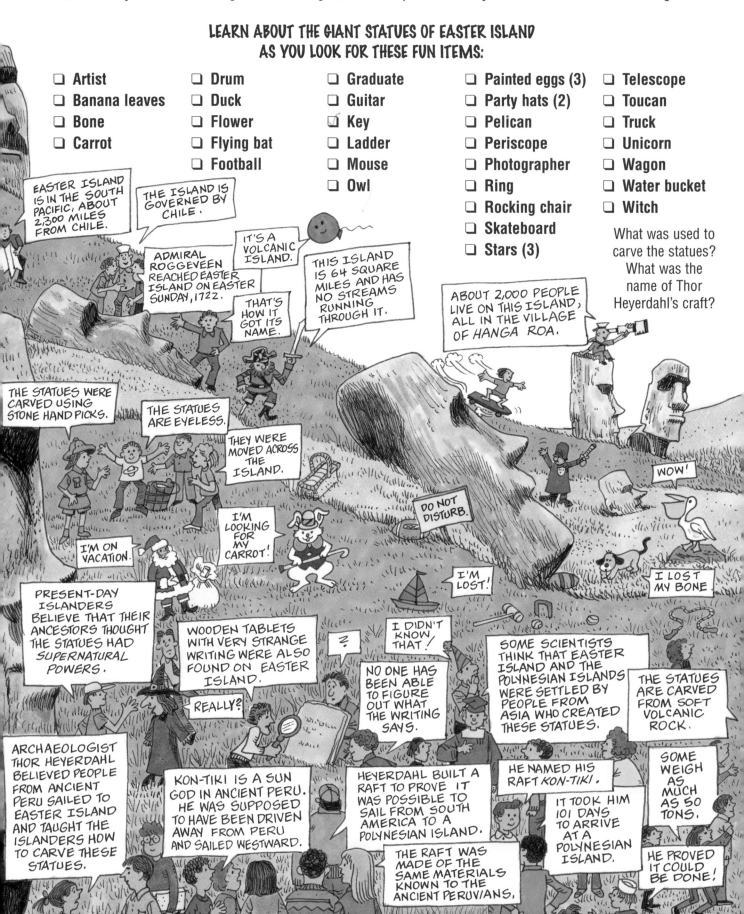

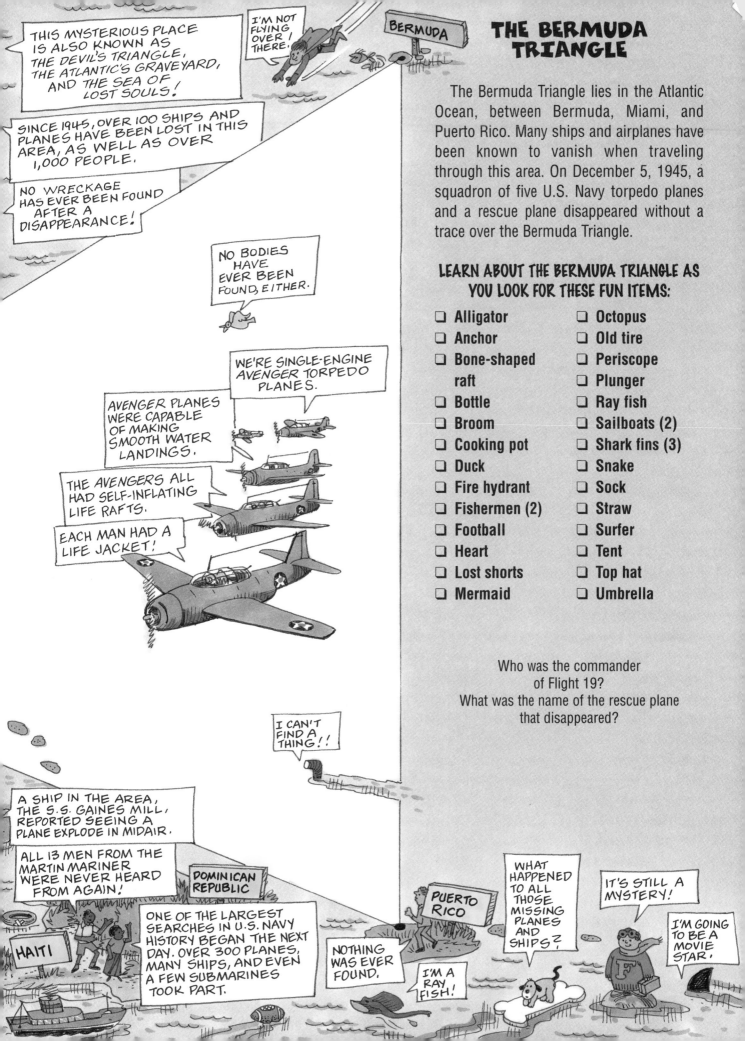

THE BERMUDA TRIANGLE

The Bermuda Triangle lies in the Atlantic Ocean, between Bermuda, Miami, and Puerto Rico. Many ships and airplanes have been known to vanish when traveling through this area. On December 5, 1945, a squadron of five U.S. Navy torpedo planes and a rescue plane disappeared without a trace over the Bermuda Triangle.

LEARN ABOUT THE BERMUDA TRIANGLE AS YOU LOOK FOR THESE FUN ITEMS:

- ❏ Alligator
- ❏ Anchor
- ❏ Bone-shaped raft
- ❏ Bottle
- ❏ Broom
- ❏ Cooking pot
- ❏ Duck
- ❏ Fire hydrant
- ❏ Fishermen (2)
- ❏ Football
- ❏ Heart
- ❏ Lost shorts
- ❏ Mermaid
- ❏ Octopus
- ❏ Old tire
- ❏ Periscope
- ❏ Plunger
- ❏ Ray fish
- ❏ Sailboats (2)
- ❏ Shark fins (3)
- ❏ Snake
- ❏ Sock
- ❏ Straw
- ❏ Surfer
- ❏ Tent
- ❏ Top hat
- ❏ Umbrella

Who was the commander of Flight 19?
What was the name of the rescue plane that disappeared?

THE LOCH NESS MONSTER

In 1933, a Scottish couple was driving along a new, modern road on the northern shore of Loch Ness. (*Loch* is the Scottish word for "lake.") Suddenly, their attention was drawn to the center of the lake. They later claimed that what they saw there was an enormous animal "rolling and plunging" in the water. Since that day, there have been more than 3,000 reported sightings of the Loch Ness monster.

LEARN ABOUT THE LOCH NESS MONSTER AS YOU LOOK FOR THESE FUN ITEMS:

- Astronaut
- Balloons (4)
- Bone
- Bucket
- Cameras (2)
- Clown
- Duck
- Fishbowl
- Flower
- Ghost
- Golfer
- Lost boot
- Mouse
- Mummy
- Net
- Note in a bottle
- Periscope
- Pig
- Sailboat
- Shorts
- Skateboard
- Star
- Sword
- Telescope
- Top hat
- Turtle

What is the monster's nickname?
How deep is Loch Ness?

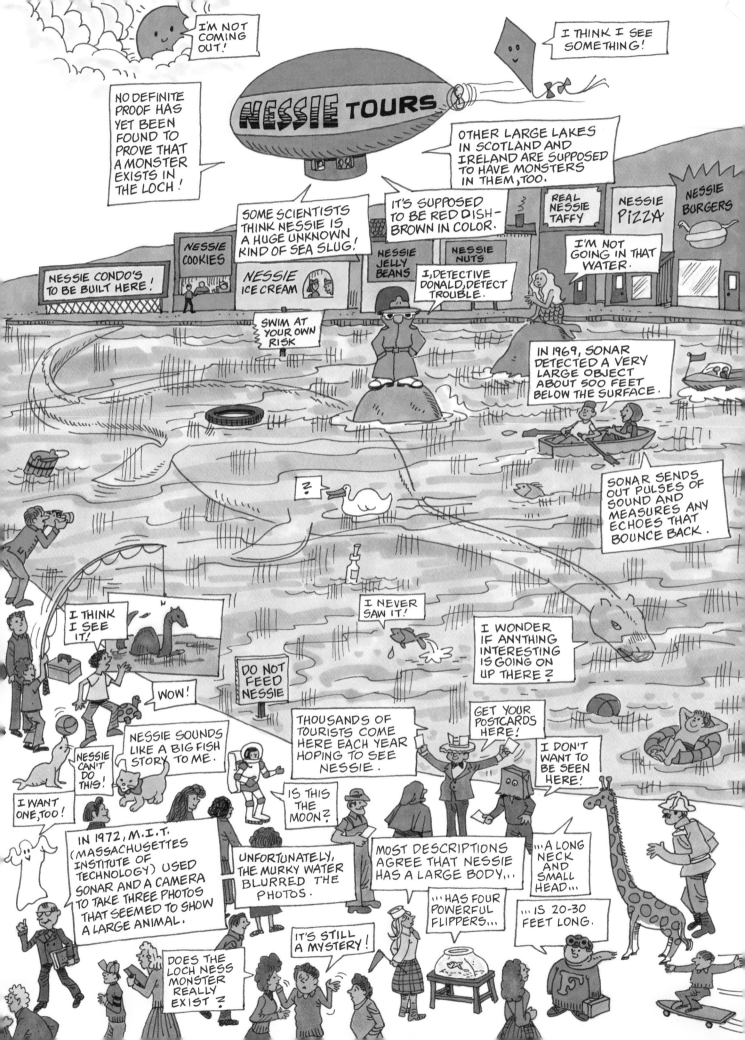

STONEHENGE

Stonehenge is an ancient monument built on Salisbury Plain in Wiltshire, England. For centuries, scientists have puzzled over the circular arrangement of this group of huge, rough-cut stones and holes in the ground. Archaeologists believe that Stonehenge was shaped and positioned by a group of people more than 3,000 years ago, without the aid of modern tools and equipment. No one knows exactly how this was accomplished.

LEARN ABOUT STONEHENGE AS YOU LOOK FOR THESE FUN ITEMS:

- ☑ Arrow
- ☐ Bird
- ☐ Bone
- ☐ Book
- ☐ Clown face
- ☐ Cooking pot
- ☑ Crown
- ☐ Cupcake
- ☐ Duck
- ☑ Elephant
- ☐ Flower
- ☐ Flying saucer
- ☐ Football
- ☐ Guitar
- ☐ Handbag
- ☐ Horse
- ☐ Jogger
- ☐ Magic wand
- ☐ Merlin
- ☐ Palm tree
- ☑ Pencil
- ☐ Pickaxe
- ☑ Pig
- ☐ Rabbit
- ☑ Shovel
- ☐ Teapot
- ☑ Tennis racket
- ☑ Turtle
- ☐ Umbrella
- ☐ Worm

How many stones were used to build Stonehenge? How much do the heaviest stones weigh?

AMELIA EARHART

In the early 20th century, flight was a new and sometimes frightening wonder. In 1908, when Amelia Earhart first saw an airplane soar among the clouds, she was fascinated by flight. Earhart became a pioneer in the new world of aviation. In 1932, she became the first woman to fly solo across the Atlantic Ocean.

LEARN ABOUT AMELIA EARHART AS YOU LOOK FOR THESE FUN ITEMS:

- ❑ Apple
- ❑ Basketball hoop
- ❑ Bell
- ❑ Chef's hat
- ❑ Envelope
- ❑ File folder
- ❑ Fish (2)
- ❑ Fishbowl
- ❑ Football
- ❑ Fork
- ❑ Graduate
- ❑ Hamburger
- ❑ Hammer
- ❑ Jack-o'-lantern
- ❑ Key
- ❑ Lost sock
- ❑ Magnifying glass
- ❑ Mouse
- ❑ Nurse
- ❑ Old-fashioned radio
- ❑ Old-fashioned telephone
- ❑ Paper airplane
- ❑ Pencil
- ❑ Pizza
- ❑ Seal
- ❑ Target
- ❑ Tennis racket
- ❑ Toaster
- ❑ TV set
- ❑ Typewriter
- ❑ Wastepaper basket
- ❑ Yo-yo

What was Amelia Earhart's great ambition as a pilot?

KING TUT'S CURSE

Howard Carter's 30-year search was over. On November 26, 1922, he stood before the entrance to the lost tomb of "the boy king," Tutankhamen *(too-tang-KAHM-un)*. Entering, Carter stared in disbelief at the gold, jewels, and other treasures before him. However, that day, a hawk—sacred symbol of pharaohs, the kings of ancient Egypt—was seen soaring above the tomb. Many people say that the hawk signalled the beginning of the pharaoh's curse.

LEARN ABOUT KING TUT'S CURSE AS YOU LOOK FOR THESE FUN ITEMS:

- ❑ Balloon
- ❑ Banana peel
- ❑ Broom
- ❑ Camel
- ❑ Crown
- ❑ Fish

- ❑ Flying bat
- ❑ Football player
- ❑ Ghost
- ❑ Horn
- ❑ Horseshoe
- ❑ Kite
- ❑ Lost medal
- ❑ Mouse

- ❑ Mummy and child
- ❑ Pencil
- ❑ Pizza deliveryman
- ❑ Sailor
- ❑ Sand
- ❑ Shovel

- ❑ Skier
- ❑ Snake
- ❑ Snowman
- ❑ Star
- ❑ Top hat
- ❑ Vase

What happened to Lord Carnarvon?
What was unusual about the scar on Tut's cheek?

ATLANTIS

The idea of a perfect world—one filled with beauty, peace, and happiness—had kept people searching for the lost island of Atlantis for centuries. Was Atlantis a real place, or just a myth of ancient Egypt made popular by Plato?

LEARN ABOUT ATLANTIS AS YOU LOOK FOR THESE FUN ITEMS:

- ❑ Ant
- ❑ Axe
- ❑ Book
- ❑ Chef's hat
- ❑ Chicken
- ❑ Deep-sea diver
- ❑ Deer
- ❑ Elephant
- ❑ Flamingo
- ❑ Frog
- ❑ Guitar
- ❑ Heart
- ❑ Ice-cream cone
- ❑ Kite
- ❑ Lion
- ❑ Mermaid
- ❑ Owl
- ❑ Ox
- ❑ Paintbrush
- ❑ Pelican
- ❑ Periscope
- ❑ Pig
- ❑ Rhinoceros
- ❑ Snail
- ❑ Snake
- ❑ Sock
- ❑ Toucan
- ❑ Turtle
- ❑ Umbrella
- ❑ Unicorn
- ❑ Zebra

Who was Plato?
Some scientists believe that
Atlantis was what island?

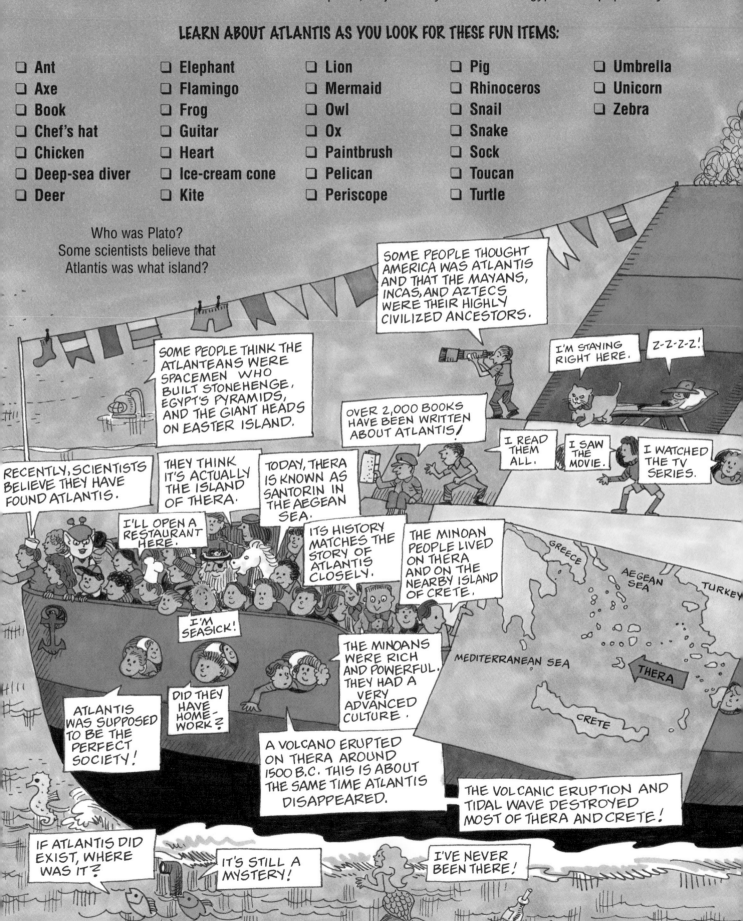

THE TUNGUSKA EXPLOSION

On June 30, 1908, the sky over the icy wilderness of Siberia flashed with a bright streak of light. Suddenly, the earth shook and smoke and fire shot up into the sky, reaching a height of 10 miles. This explosion was so tremendous, it was recorded around the world.

LEARN ABOUT THE TUNGUSKA EXPLOSION AS YOU LOOK FOR THESE FUN ITEMS:

- ❏ Arrow
- ❏ Bear
- ❏ Bell
- ❏ Boot
- ❏ Camel
- ❏ Crayon
- ❏ Crown
- ❏ Cupcake
- ❏ Doll
- ❏ Drum
- ❏ Elephant
- ❏ Fish

- ❏ Flashlight
- ❏ Flying bat
- ❏ Football
- ❏ Fork
- ❏ Ghost
- ❏ Heart
- ❏ Hot-air balloon
- ❏ Hot dog
- ❏ Igloo
- ❏ Jack-o'-lantern
- ❏ Key
- ❏ Kite

- ❏ Lips
- ❏ Mailbox
- ❏ Mask
- ❏ Mouse
- ❏ Pillow
- ❏ Ring
- ❏ Sailboat
- ❏ Skis
- ❏ Snake
- ❏ Tin can

- ❏ Tire
- ❏ Toothbrush
- ❏ Top hat
- ❏ Tree
- ❏ Tulip
- ❏ Turtle

What is a meteorite? When were atomic bombs first produced?

THE MARY CELESTE

People said that the *Mary Celeste* was "born" unlucky. This sailing ship, built in 1861, originally was named the *Amazon*. It went through four captains and numerous catastrophes before it was bought by an American and renamed the *Mary Celeste*. In November 1872, Benjamin Briggs, the new captain and part-owner, along with his family and crew, set sail from New York to Genoa, Italy. However, he, his family, and crew all disappeared en route. The *Mary Celeste* was later found in good condition but, to this day, no one knows what happened on that mysterious voyage.

LEARN ABOUT THE MARY CELESTE AS YOU LOOK FOR THESE FUN ITEMS:

- ☐ Balloons (4)
- ☐ Barrel
- ☐ Broom
- ☐ Cactus
- ☐ Chattering teeth
- ☐ Chef's hat
- ☐ Duck
- ☐ Elephant
- ☐ Fishing pole
- ☐ Flamingo
- ☐ Flowerpot
- ☐ Flying bats (2)
- ☐ Ghost
- ☐ Giraffe
- ☐ Horseshoe
- ☐ Hot dog
- ☐ Humpty Dumpty
- ☐ Mouse
- ☐ Octopus
- ☐ Pelican
- ☐ Periscope
- ☐ Saw
- ☐ Skull and crossbones
- ☐ Sock
- ☐ Surfboard
- ☐ Telescope
- ☐ Turtle
- ☐ Umbrella
- ☐ Whale

What cargo was the *Mary Celeste* carrying? Where was the ship headed when everyone aboard disappeared?

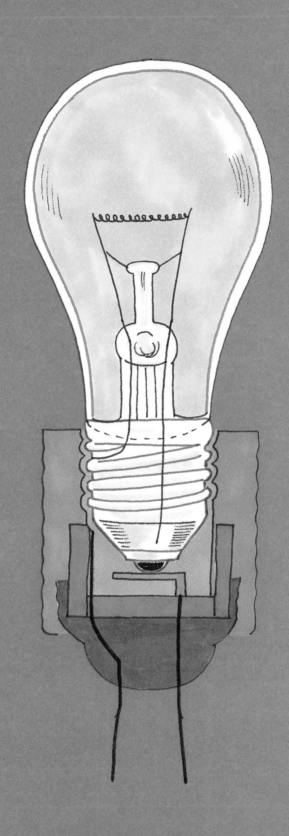

HOW THINGS WORK

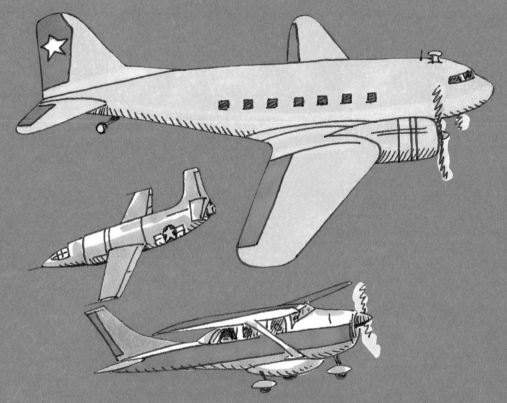

COMPUTERS

Rare just a generation ago, computers are now everywhere! As technological know-how improves, these devices keep getting smaller, faster, more reliable, and easier to use.

LEARN ABOUT COMPUTERS AS YOU LOOK FOR THESE FUN ITEMS:

- ☐ Bears (2)
- ☐ Birds (2)
- ☐ Fish (3)
- ☐ Flowers (2)
- ☐ Ghosts (3)
- ☐ Horses (2)
- ☐ Neckerchief
- ☐ Pencils (2)
- ☐ Scarves (2)
- ☐ Sheet of paper
- ☐ Snail
- ☐ Snake
- ☐ Sunglasses (2)
- ☐ Volcanoes (2)

What is another word for modulator/demodulator?
What do *RAM* and *ROM* stand for?

DATA USED BY COMPUTERS ARE STORED ON VARIOUS TYPES OF DEVICES KNOWN AS DISKS. EACH COMPUTER HAS A HARD DISK, WHERE PROGRAMS, FILES, DOCUMENTS, AND OTHER KEY INFORMATION ARE STORED.

DATA STORED ON A COMPUTER'S HARD DRIVE CAN BE COPIED TO REMOVABLE DISKS AND STORED ELSEWHERE. FLOPPY DISKS, CDS, ZIP DISKS, AND DVDS ARE WIDELY USED STORAGE MEDIA.

A MICROCHIP IS A TINY BUT POWERFUL DEVICE THAT CAN HOLD AN IMMENSE AMOUNT OF DATA. AS MICROCHIPS HAVE GOTTEN SMALLER WHILE HOLDING MORE DATA, COMPUTERS HAVE BECOME SMALLER, TOO.

HARDWARE THAT YOU CAN SEE INCLUDES THE SYSTEM UNIT (CPU), MONITOR, KEYBOARD, MOUSE, AND STORAGE DEVICES (SUCH AS FLOPPY DISK, CD-ROM, OR DVD DRIVES).

A PERSONAL COMPUTER (PC) IS ONE THAT IS MEANT TO BE USED BY ONLY ONE PERSON AT A TIME. MOST PEOPLE USE THE WORD *PC* TO DESCRIBE A DESKTOP COMPUTER, BUT LAPTOP AND HAND-HELD COMPUTERS ARE ALSO ONE-PERSON-AT-A-TIME DEVICES.

HARDWARE THAT YOU CAN'T SEE—BECAUSE IT'S INSIDE THE SYSTEM UNIT—INCLUDES THE PROCESSOR AND MEMORY CHIPS.

A KEYBOARD IS USED LIKE A TYPEWRITER. WHEN YOU PRESS A KEY, INFORMATION APPEARS ON THE SCREEN.

THE SCANNER IS LIKE A CAMERA AND COPY MACHINE ROLLED INTO ONE DEVICE. USING LIGHT, MIRRORS, AND LENSES, IT TURNS AN IMAGE INTO DATA THAT YOUR COMPUTER CAN USE.

PROGRAMS FOR WORD PROCESSING, WEB BROWSING, E-MAIL, PLAYING GAMES, AND MAKING SPREAD-SHEETS OR DATABASES ARE ALL EXAMPLES OF SOFTWARE.

DO THEY STILL USE PENCILS?

YOUR COMPUTER MAY HAVE OTHER HARDWARE CALLED *PERIPHERALS*—DEVICES INSTALLED IN OR ATTACHED TO YOUR COMPUTER TO EXPAND WHAT IT CAN DO. COMMON PERIPHERALS INCLUDE MODEMS, PRINTERS, AND SCANNERS.

THE MODEM IS A DEVICE THAT LETS TWO OR MORE COMPUTERS "TALK" TO EACH OTHER. MODEMS SEND SIGNALS THROUGH TELEPHONE, CABLE, OR OTHER COMMUNICATIONS LINES. (MODEM IS SHORT FOR "*MO*dulator/ *DEM*odulator.")

FOR A COMPUTER TO WORK, YOU NEED BOTH HARDWARE AND SOFTWARE. HARDWARE IS THE EQUIPMENT THAT DOES THE WORK. SOFTWARE IS INFORMATION THAT TELLS THE EQUIPMENT WHAT TO DO AND HOW TO DO IT.

LIGHT BULBS

An electric light bulb is a glass bulb that contains a filament, an inert gas, and electrical contacts. Light is produced when an electrical current passes through the filament. This current heats the filament to a temperature that is high enough to produce light.

Thomas Edison invented the light bulb in 1879.

LEARN HOW LIGHT BULBS WORK AS YOU LOOK FOR THESE FUN ITEMS:

- ❑ Alarm clock
- ❑ Apple
- ❑ Baby's bib
- ❑ Baseball bat
- ❑ Bone
- ❑ Burned-out bulb
- ❑ Candles (2)
- ❑ Clipboard

- ❑ Clown
- ❑ Crayon
- ❑ Elephant
- ❑ Envelope
- ❑ Fish (2)
- ❑ Flowers (2)
- ❑ Football
- ❑ Fork

- ❑ Ghost
- ❑ Heart
- ❑ Helmet
- ❑ Horse's head
- ❑ Horseshoe
- ❑ Hose
- ❑ Jump rope
- ❑ Necktie

- ❑ Paintbrush
- ❑ Paper bag
- ❑ Pencil
- ❑ Pizza box
- ❑ Saw
- ❑ Tepee
- ❑ Used tire
- ❑ Vest

What is a filament made of?
What determines the brightness of a light bulb?

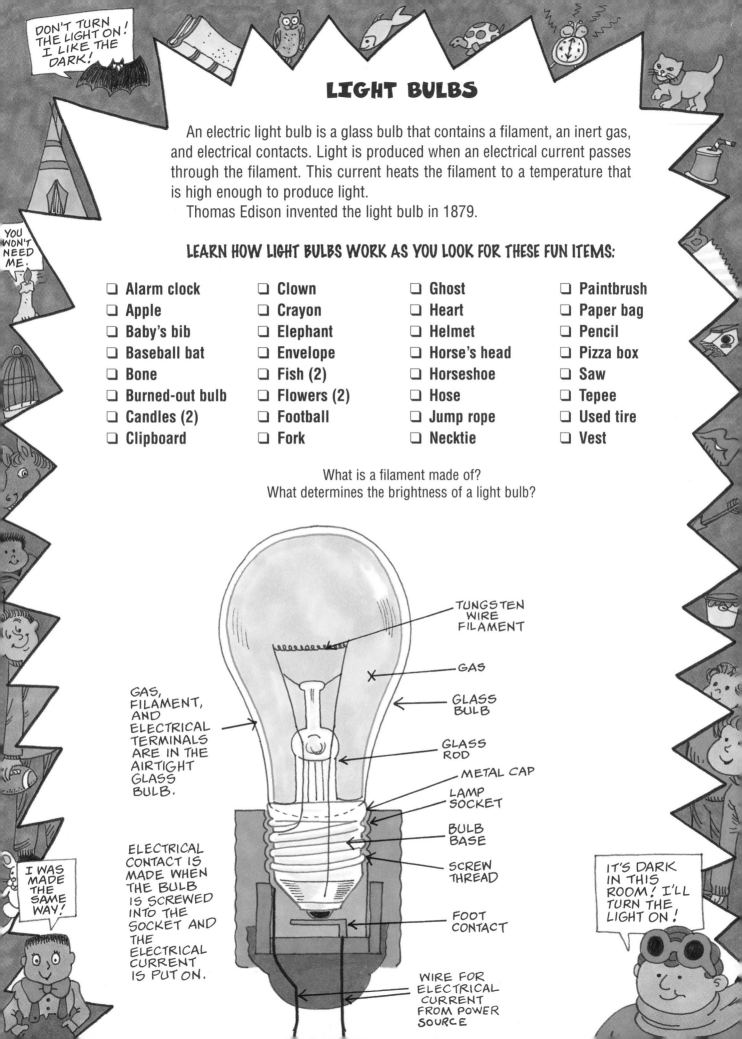

DON'T TURN THE LIGHT ON! I LIKE THE DARK!

YOU WON'T NEED ME.

I WAS MADE THE SAME WAY!

IT'S DARK IN THIS ROOM! I'LL TURN THE LIGHT ON!

TUNGSTEN WIRE FILAMENT

GAS

GLASS BULB

GLASS ROD

METAL CAP

LAMP SOCKET

BULB BASE

SCREW THREAD

FOOT CONTACT

GAS, FILAMENT, AND ELECTRICAL TERMINALS ARE IN THE AIRTIGHT GLASS BULB.

ELECTRICAL CONTACT IS MADE WHEN THE BULB IS SCREWED INTO THE SOCKET AND THE ELECTRICAL CURRENT IS PUT ON.

WIRE FOR ELECTRICAL CURRENT FROM POWER SOURCE

SUBMARINES

A submarine is designed to travel under water. Aided by small moveable fins called *hydroplanes*, it dives and surfaces by filling its ballast tanks with water or air. When the tanks are filled with water, the sub gets heavier and sinks. When compressed air is blown into the tanks, forcing out the water, the sub gets lighter and rises. Power to drive the sub comes from a nuclear reactor or from a combination of diesel and battery-driven engines.

LEARN HOW SUBS WORK AS YOU LOOK FOR THESE FUN ITEMS:

- ❑ Bathtub
- ❑ Book
- ❑ Cactus
- ❑ Clothespins (2)
- ❑ Crown
- ❑ Fish hook
- ❑ Four-leaf clover
- ❑ Frog
- ❑ Ghost
- ❑ Hammer
- ❑ Jellyfish
- ❑ Light bulb
- ❑ Mermaid
- ❑ Mouse
- ❑ Pizza
- ❑ Propellers (3)
- ❑ Sea horse
- ❑ Tuba

What was the *Turtle*? What do hydroplanes do?

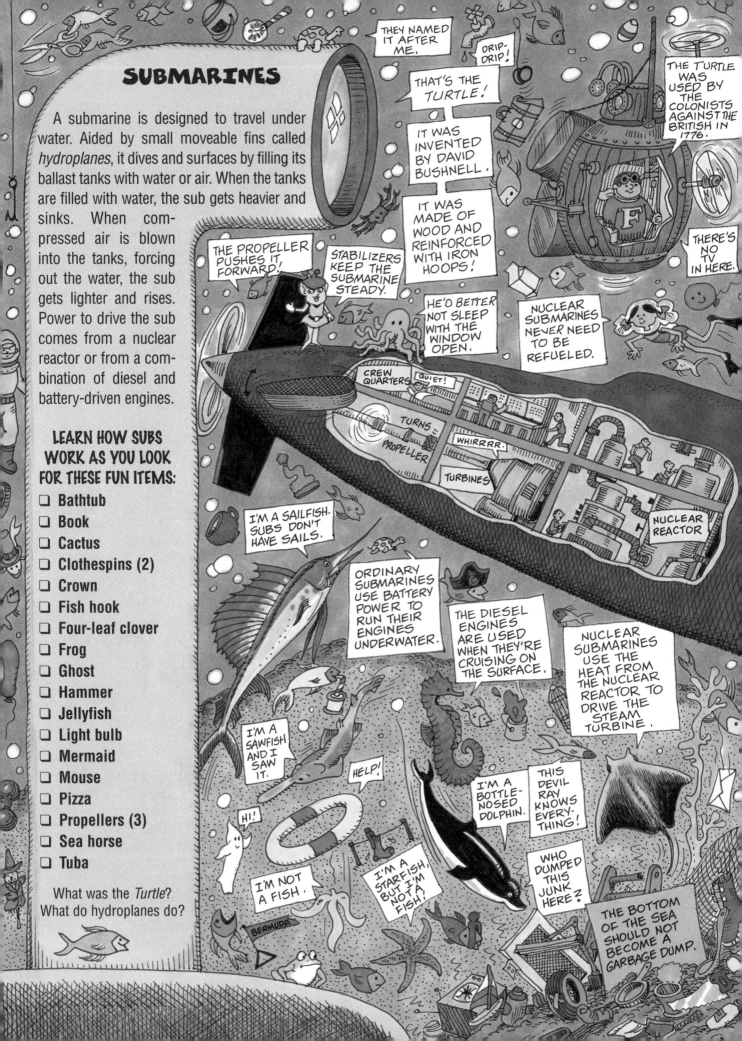

HELICOPTERS

Helicopters can fly straight up or down, forward or backward, or sideways; and they can even hover in place. Their mobility allows them to fly into places that airplanes cannot.

The first helicopter to achieve flight was built in France in 1907. It was not reliable, however. In 1939, Igor Sikorsky developed the first successful one, and the modern era of helicopters began.

LEARN HOW HELICOPTERS WORK AS YOU LOOK FOR THESE FUN ITEMS:

- ❏ Balloon
- ❏ Bee
- ❏ Book
- ❏ Bucket
- ❏ Butterfly
- ❏ Cactus
- ❏ Camera
- ❏ Candy cane
- ❏ Canteen

- ❏ Flying bat
- ❏ Frog
- ❏ Heart
- ❏ Jack-o'-lantern
- ❏ Lollipop
- ❏ Medal
- ❏ Mouse
- ❏ Oilcan
- ❏ Owl

- ❏ Paper airplane
- ❏ Penguin
- ❏ Periscope
- ❏ Roller skates
- ❏ Schoolbag
- ❏ Screwdriver
- ❏ Squirrel
- ❏ Tennis racket

How many main rotor blades do most helicopters have?
What gives a helicopter its power?

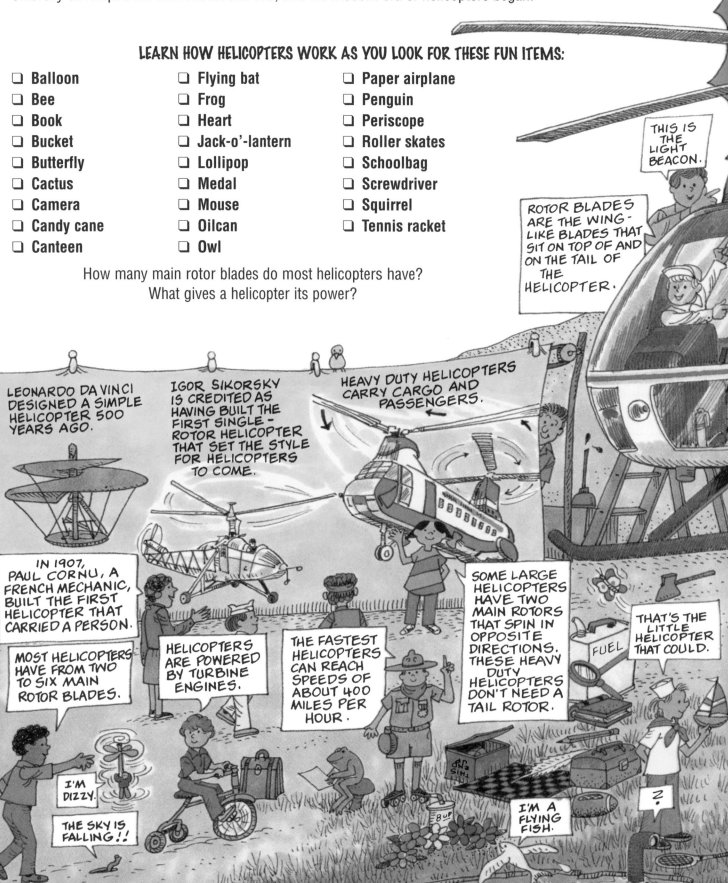

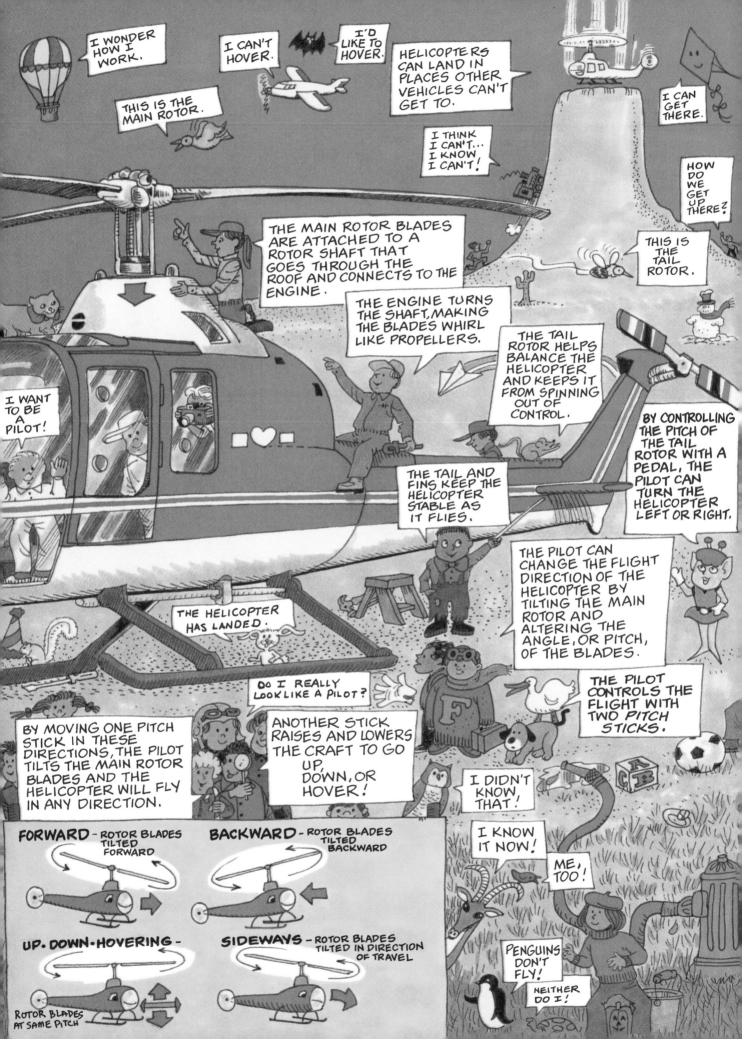

ORCHESTRAS

An orchestra is not a random gathering of musicians and their instruments. It is a carefully planned group of different types of instruments, with each one having its own part to play in the performance.

LEARN HOW ORCHESTRAS WORK AS YOU LOOK FOR THESE FUN ITEMS:

- ☐ Ball of string
- ☐ Balloon
- ☐ Baseball cap
- ☐ Bird
- ☐ Broom
- ☐ Brush
- ☐ Candle
- ☐ Duck
- ☐ Earring

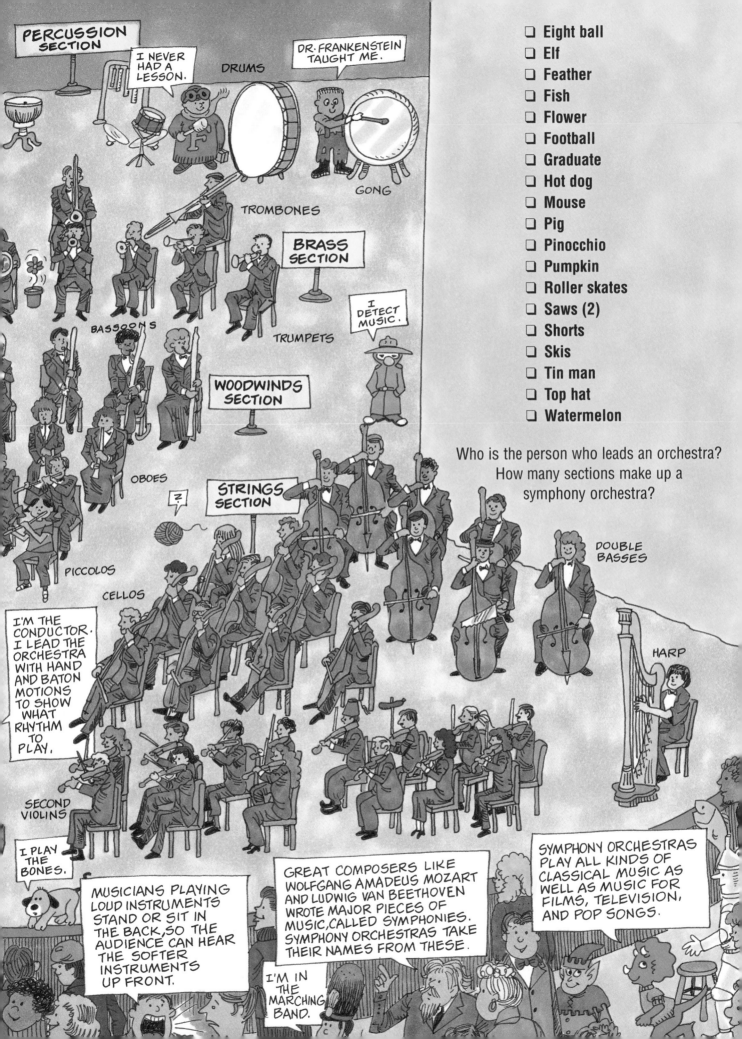

Who is the person who leads an orchestra? How many sections make up a symphony orchestra?

CDS AND DVDS

Whether it's music or movies that you love best, CDs and DVDs make it possible for you to take your favorite tunes and flicks almost anywhere. Those data-packed little plastic disks are a marvel of modern technology.

LEARN ABOUT CDs AND DVDs AS YOU LOOK FOR THESE FUN ITEMS:

- ❑ Apple
- ❑ Balloons (2)
- ❑ Banana peel
- ❑ Boat in a bottle
- ❑ Book
- ❑ Bowling ball
- ❑ Broom
- ❑ Butterfly
- ❑ Candle
- ❑ Clown
- ❑ Crown
- ❑ Donkey
- ❑ Flower
- ❑ Flying saucer
- ❑ Football
- ❑ Hairbrush
- ❑ Jack-o'-lantern
- ❑ Magnifying glass
- ❑ Paper airplane
- ❑ Picnic basket
- ❑ Scarves (2)
- ❑ Scissors
- ❑ Shovel
- ❑ Tent

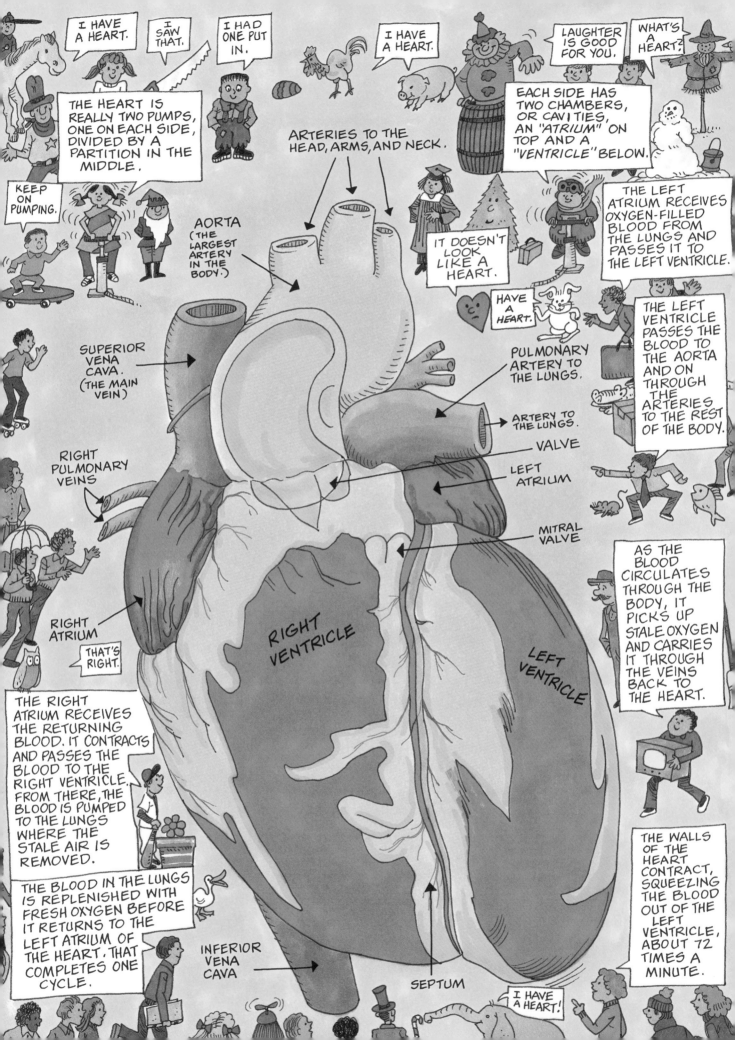

THE HUMAN HEART

A heart is a muscular pump that circulates blood through the blood vessels. The blood carries nourishment and oxygen to every part of the body. In one year, the human heart pumps about 650,000 gallons of blood, enough to fill 50 swimming pools!

LEARN HOW THE HUMAN HEART WORKS AS YOU LOOK FOR THESE FUN ITEMS:

- ☐ Ball
- ☐ Banana peel
- ☐ Barrel
- ☐ Baseball hat
- ☐ Book
- ☐ Candy cane
- ☐ Chicken
- ☐ Dracula
- ☐ Drum
- ☐ Duck
- ☐ Flower
- ☐ Joggers (2)
- ☐ Lion
- ☐ Microscope
- ☐ Mouse
- ☐ Mustache
- ☐ Owl
- ☐ Pillow
- ☐ Propeller
- ☐ Roller skates
- ☐ Saw
- ☐ Singer
- ☐ Skateboard
- ☐ Stars (2)
- ☐ Top hat
- ☐ TV set
- ☐ Umbrella
- ☐ Worm

What are the heart's chambers called?
Approximately how long does it take for the blood to travel throughout the body?

SOLAR ENERGY

Solar energy is power produced by the sun. It can be used to heat and purify water, give power to engines, and produce electricity. A person would have to burn 550 billion tons of coal in order to equal the amount of solar energy received by Earth in one day!

LEARN HOW SOLAR ENERGY WORKS AS YOU LOOK FOR THESE FUN ITEMS:

- ☐ Apple
- ☐ Arrow
- ☐ Baseball
- ☐ Basketball hoop
- ☐ Bone
- ☐ Bowling ball
- ☐ Brush
- ☐ Buckets (2)
- ☐ Doghouse
- ☐ Duck
- ☐ Earmuffs
- ☐ Fire hydrant
- ☐ Flower
- ☐ Football
- ☐ Hammer
- ☐ Heart
- ☐ Helmet
- ☐ Kite
- ☐ Mailbox
- ☐ Newspaper
- ☐ Rabbit
- ☐ Screwdriver
- ☐ Star
- ☐ Turtle
- ☐ Umbrella
- ☐ Umpire
- ☐ Watering can
- ☐ Worm

What is solar power most commonly used for?
Why are the insides of solar panels painted black?

AIRPLANES

Airplanes are fascinating pieces of machinery that soar through the air. Whether passenger, private, or military, they all operate under the same aerodynamic principles.

The first power-driven flight was made by the Wright brothers at Kitty Hawk, North Carolina, in 1903.

LEARN HOW AIRPLANES WORK AS YOU LOOK FOR THESE FUN ITEMS:

- ☐ "X-1"
- ☐ Acrobat
- ☐ Banana
- ☐ Bowling ball
- ☐ Broom
- ☐ Elephant
- ☐ Fishing pole
- ☐ Flowers (3)

- ☐ Flying carpet
- ☐ Flying horse
- ☐ Flying saucer
- ☐ Football
- ☐ Ghost
- ☐ Glider
- ☐ Hamburger
- ☐ Hang glider

- ☐ Kite
- ☐ Mouse
- ☐ Paper airplane
- ☐ Pencil
- ☐ Pinwheel
- ☐ Pizza
- ☐ Sailboat
- ☐ Seaplane

- ☐ Sled
- ☐ Stars (2)
- ☐ Superheroes (2)
- ☐ Surfboard
- ☐ Umbrella
- ☐ Yo-yo

What provides an airplane's lift?
What kind of engine "pulls" the airplane through the air?

FLAPS ON BOTH WINGS MOVE TO STEER PLANE.

IN 1891, OTTO LILIENTHAL, A GERMAN, BECAME THE FIRST PERSON TO FLY SUCCESSFULLY IN A HANG-GLIDER.

I'M HITCHING A RIDE.

PUNT!

USUALLY, THE GREATER THE WEIGHT OF THE AIRPLANE THE LARGER THE WINGS WILL BE.

TAILFIN

RUDDER

TAIL FLAPS MOVE TO STEER AIRPLANE

I'M NOT A FLYING SAUCER!

747

POST NO BILLS

I DON'T HAVE AN ENGINE.

IT'S EASY TO FLY.

WHERE'S THE SURF?

AN AIRPLANE'S LIFT IS PROVIDED BY THE WINGS.

I HAVE NO FUEL PROBLEM.

STABILIZER

SEAPLANES CAN LAND ON THE WATER.

A WING IS ROUNDED ON TOP AND FLAT ON THE BOTTOM.

THE ENGINE PROVIDES THE THRUST, OR FORCE, NECESSARY FOR TAKEOFF. WHILE AIRBORNE, ITS POWER MAINTAINS AND CHANGES THE AIRPLANE'S SPEED.

LOWER AIR PRESSURE

WING

LIFT

TURBOJET ENGINE

COMBUSTION CHAMBER

IGNITER

FUEL NOZZLE

EXHAUST GASES

AIR INTAKE

JET NOZZLE

COMPRESSOR

HELLO EARTHLINGS!

I DIDN'T KNOW THAT!

THE AIR FLOWING OVER THE ROUNDED PART TRAVELS A GREATER DISTANCE THAN THE AIR FLOWING PAST THE FLAT PART. THE AIR ABOVE MOVES FASTER AND LOSES PRESSURE AS IT "STRETCHES OUT" GOING OVER THE ROUNDED SECTION.

LASERS

A laser is a device that intensifies or increases light. It produces a thin beam of light, stronger than sunlight, that can burn a hole through diamond or steel.

The first operational laser was built in 1960.

LEARN HOW LASERS WORK AS YOU LOOK FOR THESE FUN ITEMS:

- ❑ Apple
- ❑ Book
- ❑ Cheerleader
- ❑ Chicken
- ❑ Clock
- ❑ Drinking straw
- ❑ Drum
- ❑ Electrodes (2)
- ❑ Envelope
- ❑ Fish tank
- ❑ Flamingo
- ❑ Football
- ❑ Frog
- ❑ Globe
- ❑ Hot dog
- ❑ Little Red Riding Hood
- ❑ Necktie
- ❑ Orangutan
- ❑ Painted egg
- ❑ Paper airplane
- ❑ Parrot
- ❑ Rabbit
- ❑ Roller skates
- ❑ Stapler
- ❑ Stethoscope
- ❑ Thermometer
- ❑ Umbrella
- ❑ Vase

Name two types of lasers.
What are some of the uses of laser beams?

IN ORDINARY LIGHT, SUCH AS THAT FROM A LIGHT BULB, THE LIGHT WAVES GO OUT IN MANY DIFFERENT DIRECTIONS.

IN A LASER BEAM, THE LIGHT WAVES ALL HAVE THE SAME LENGTH AND TRAVEL IN THE SAME DIRECTION, PRODUCING A NARROW, INTENSE BEAM OF LIGHT.

HOORAY FOR LASERS!

IS THIS THE GYM CLASS?

I'M IN THE MARCHING BAND.

IS IT TIME FOR LUNCH?

I DON'T NEED A GAS MASK.

I WANT ONE.

LASERS COME IN MANY SHAPES AND SIZES.

SOLID-STATE LASERS USE A MATERIAL SUCH AS RUBY, EMERALD, OR GLASS CRYSTAL TO PRODUCE BURSTS OF LIGHT.

GAS LASERS ARE MADE IN A GAS-FILLED TUBE AND PRODUCE A CONTINUOUS BEAM OF LIGHT.

GAS LASER

GAS-FILLED TUBE

ELECTRODE

ELECTRODE

SEMI-SILVERED MIRROR

MIRROR

THE MATERIAL USED TO CREATE LASER LIGHT IS CALLED A "MEDIUM." IT MAY BE SOLID, GAS, OR EVEN LIQUID.

TO PRODUCE A BEAM OF LASER LIGHT, ENERGY FROM A POWER SOURCE, SUCH AS AN ELECTRIC CURRENT, EXCITES THE ATOMS OF THE MEDIUM CAUSING THEM TO STRIKE EACH OTHER AND GIVE OFF LIGHT.

I'LL PUNCH YOU IN THE NOSE!

I DON'T HAVE A NOSE.

MIRRORS ARE USED WITHIN THE LASER TUBE TO INCREASE THE LIGHT-PRODUCING ATOM.

ONCE THE LIGHT IS BRIGHT ENOUGH, IT PASSES THROUGH A SEMI-SILVERED MIRROR AND LEAVES THE LASER.

MAGNETS AND MAGNETISM

A magnet is often thought of as a toy that can pull or pick up metal objects. However, the invisible force of magnetism is used in a wide variety of modern devices.

Magnetite, an iron ore with magnetic properties, was used as a compass by early sailors to navigate.

LEARN HOW MAGNETS AND MAGNETISM WORK AS YOU LOOK FOR THESE FUN ITEMS:

- ❏ Bent nail
- ❏ Cactus
- ❏ Clown
- ❏ Compasses (2)
- ❏ Dart
- ❏ Duck
- ❏ Flower
- ❏ Football player
- ❏ Hard hats (2)
- ❏ Hooks (2)
- ❏ Hot dog
- ❏ Ice-cream cone
- ❏ Kangaroo
- ❏ Key
- ❏ Lion
- ❏ Mermaid
- ❏ Mouse
- ❏ Periscope
- ❏ Pillow
- ❏ Ringmaster
- ❏ Rocking chair
- ❏ Safety pin
- ❏ Sewing needle
- ❏ Shovel
- ❏ Snake
- ❏ Spoon
- ❏ Tin Man
- ❏ TV antenna

When is a metal magnetized?
Where are Earth's two magnetic poles?

I'M STAYING RIGHT HERE.

I THINK I'LL PLANT MAGNETS IN MY FIELD NEXT SPRING.

A MAGNETIC FIELD IS THE INVISIBLE FORCE WHICH GIVES THE MAGNET THE ABILITY TO ATTRACT OTHER STEEL OR IRON OBJECTS.

HELP!

8 UP

I'M FILING A COMPLAINT.

THE MAGNET DOESN'T AFFECT ME!

A BUSY DAY.

ELECTROMAGNETS ARE USED IN ELECTRIC MOTORS.

IN LOUD SPEAKERS.

IN TAPE AND VIDEO RECORDER

IN TELEPHONES

z

THE MAGNET DIDN'T GET ME YET.

ME, TOO!

ME, THREE!

A MAGNET CAN STILL RETAIN ITS MAGNETISM IF IT IS CUT IN HALF AS LONG AS THE DOMAINS WITHIN EACH PIECE STAY ALIGNED.

EACH MAGNET HAS A NORTH POLE(N) AND A SOUTH POLE(S).

WHEN THE MAGNETIC FIELDS OF TWO DIFFERENT MAGNETS COME TOGETHER, THEY WILL EITHER REPEL OR ATTRACT.

THE SOUTH POLE OF ONE MAGNET WILL ATTRACT THE NORTH POLE OF ANOTHER MAGNET. IF THE TWO POLES ARE THE SAME, THE MAGNETS WILL REPEL ONE ANOTHER.

N S

S N

S S

N N

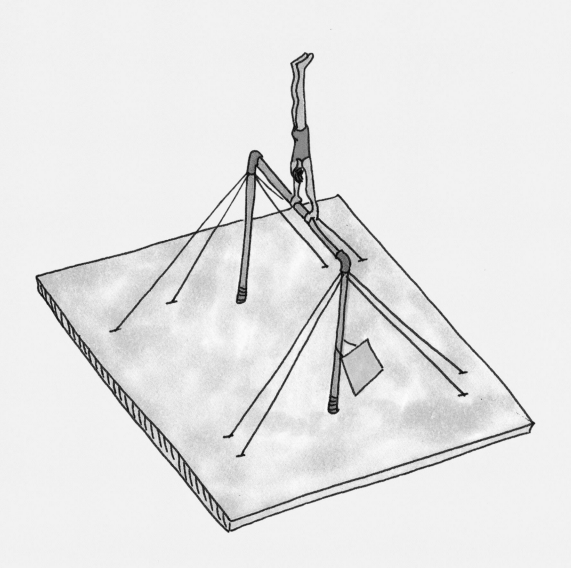

Sports

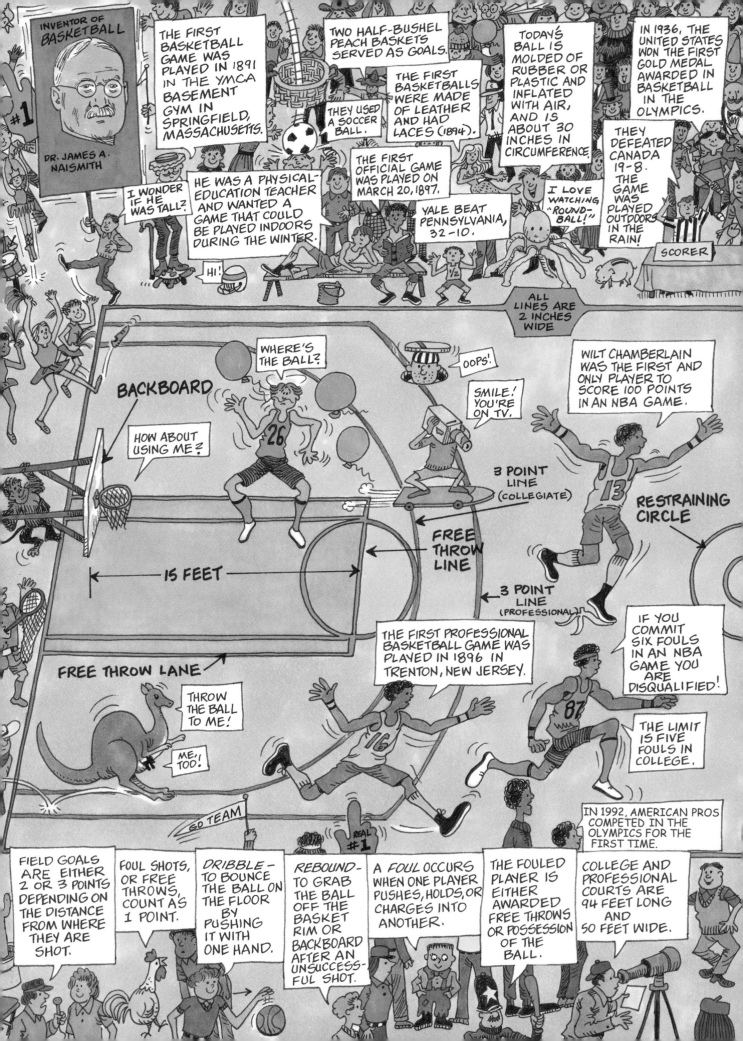

BASKETBALL

Basketball is played in more than 200 countries around the world. To play, all you need are a ball, a basket or hoop, and a level surface. Basketball can be played indoors or out, alone or with others, at night or by day, 365 days a year!

LEARN ABOUT BASKETBALL AS YOU LOOK FOR THESE FUN ITEMS:

- ☐ Balloons (5)
- ☐ Banana peel
- ☐ Bowling ball
- ☐ Boxing glove
- ☐ Bucket
- ☐ Cane
- ☐ Clock
- ☐ Crown
- ☐ Football
- ☐ Graduate
- ☐ Ice skate
- ☐ Kite
- ☐ Lost shoe
- ☐ Mermaid
- ☐ Monkey
- ☐ Mouse
- ☐ Pencil
- ☐ Piggy bank
- ☐ Scarecrow
- ☐ Skateboard
- ☐ Soccer ball
- ☐ Top hat
- ☐ Turtle

Name the NBA's career scoring leader.

GYMNASTICS

In gymnastics, acrobatic exercises are performed on various pieces of equipment. Gymnastics helps develop balance, agility, and strength. During the Olympics of 1972 and 1976, the emergence of two superstars—Olga Korbut and Nadia Comaneci—helped give gymnastics worldwide popularity.

LEARN ABOUT GYMNASTICS AS YOU LOOK FOR THESE FUN ITEMS:

- ☐ Banana peel
- ☐ Bear
- ☐ Broom
- ☐ Crutch
- ☐ Duck
- ☐ Elephant
- ☐ Juggler
- ☐ Kangaroo
- ☐ Mail carrier
- ☐ Pillow
- ☐ Scarecrow
- ☐ Snowman
- ☐ Star
- ☐ Telescope
- ☐ TV camera
- ☐ Unicorn
- ☐ Water skier

Who was the first Olympic gymnast to earn a perfect 10? Name the eight events in which men compete.

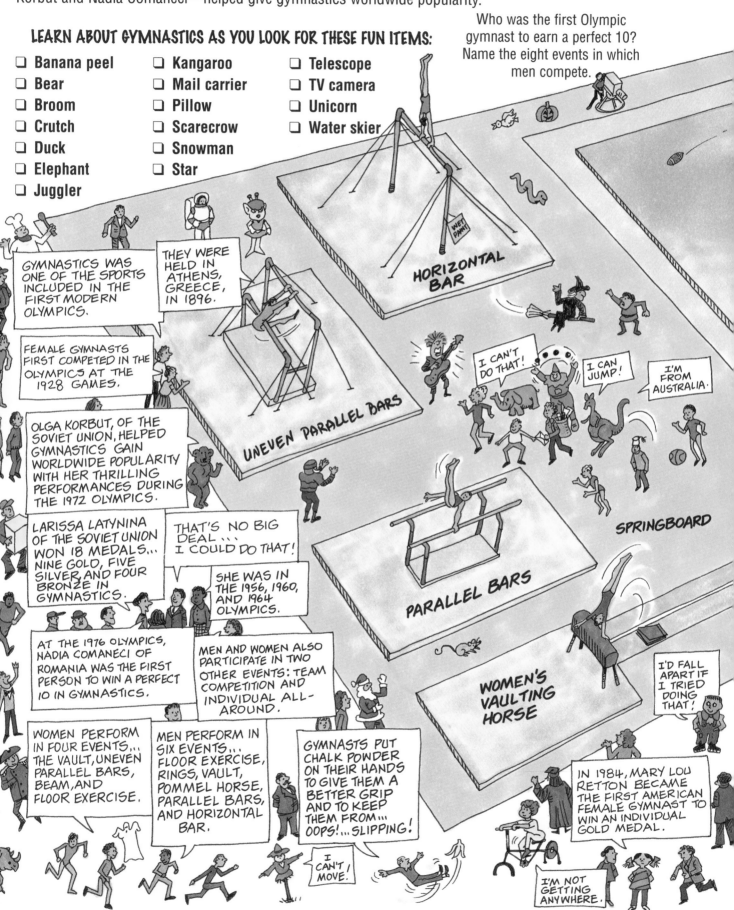

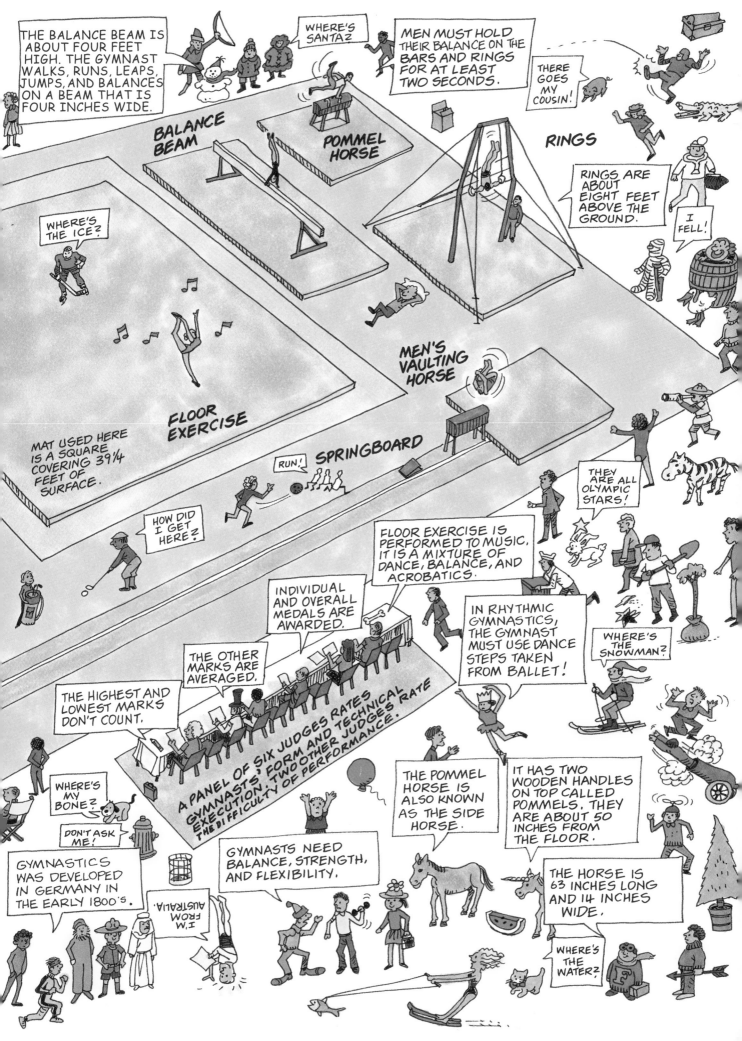

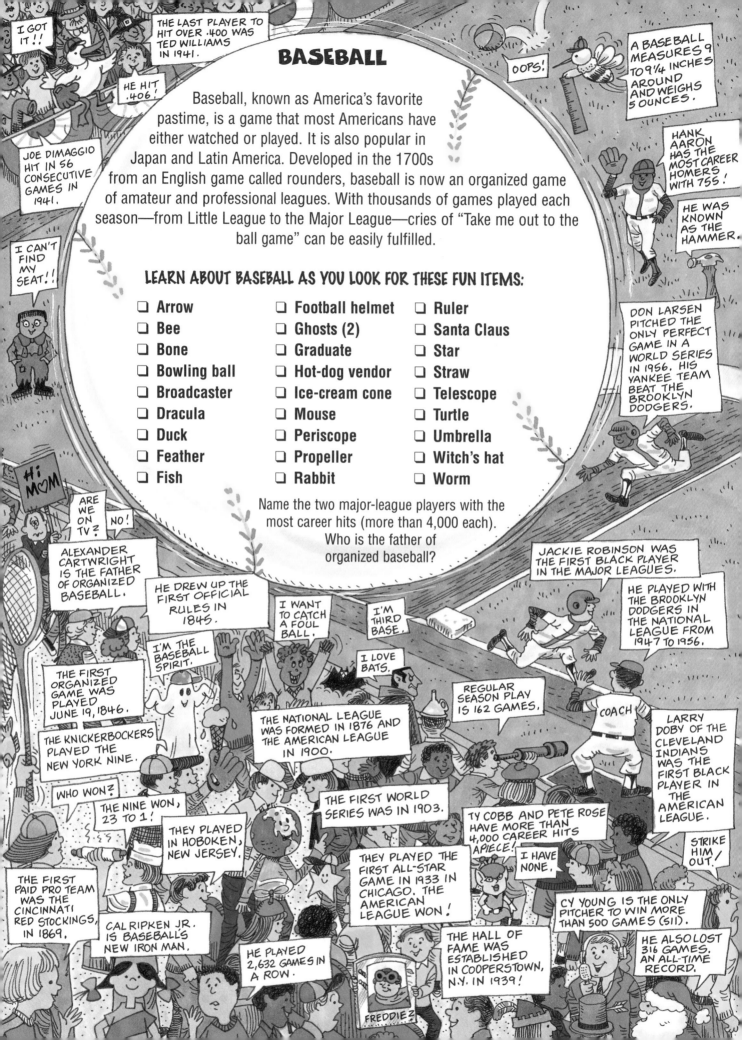

BASEBALL

Baseball, known as America's favorite pastime, is a game that most Americans have either watched or played. It is also popular in Japan and Latin America. Developed in the 1700s from an English game called rounders, baseball is now an organized game of amateur and professional leagues. With thousands of games played each season—from Little League to the Major League—cries of "Take me out to the ball game" can be easily fulfilled.

LEARN ABOUT BASEBALL AS YOU LOOK FOR THESE FUN ITEMS:

- ❑ Arrow
- ❑ Bee
- ❑ Bone
- ❑ Bowling ball
- ❑ Broadcaster
- ❑ Dracula
- ❑ Duck
- ❑ Feather
- ❑ Fish
- ❑ Football helmet
- ❑ Ghosts (2)
- ❑ Graduate
- ❑ Hot-dog vendor
- ❑ Ice-cream cone
- ❑ Mouse
- ❑ Periscope
- ❑ Propeller
- ❑ Rabbit
- ❑ Ruler
- ❑ Santa Claus
- ❑ Star
- ❑ Straw
- ❑ Telescope
- ❑ Turtle
- ❑ Umbrella
- ❑ Witch's hat
- ❑ Worm

Name the two major-league players with the most career hits (more than 4,000 each). Who is the father of organized baseball?

NASCAR RACING

NASCAR racing is fast becoming one of the most popular spectator sports in the U.S. With more than 7 million fans a year attending at NASCAR events, not all of the roars you'll hear at the track are coming from the car engines!

LEARN ABOUT NASCAR RACING AS YOU LOOK FOR THESE FUN ITEMS:

- ❑ Astronaut
- ❑ Balloon
- ❑ Birds (2)
- ❑ Bone
- ❑ Elephant
- ❑ Fish
- ❑ Flowers
- ❑ Heart
- ❑ Jockey
- ❑ Kangaroo
- ❑ Kite
- ❑ Pirate
- ❑ Rabbit
- ❑ Sailboat
- ❑ Scuba diver
- ❑ Oilcan
- ❑ Table
- ❑ Tepee
- ❑ Turtle

How long is the Daytona International Speedway?
Who won the first race there?

FOOTBALL

On November 6, 1869, the universities of Rutgers and Princeton met in New Brunswick, New Jersey, in the first college football game. Rutgers won it, 6–4.

The early games were a modified version of soccer and rugby. Football pioneers, such as Walter Camp, instituted 11-man teams, downs and yards to go, a smaller field, the line of scrimmage, and a new system of scoring.

LEARN ABOUT FOOTBALL AS YOU LOOK FOR THESE FUN ITEMS:

- ☐ Air pump
- ☐ Arrow
- ☐ Birds (3)
- ☐ Blimp
- ☐ Bowling pin
- ☐ Candy cane
- ☐ Clipboard
- ☐ Fish
- ☐ Flying bat
- ☐ Ghost
- ☐ Hamburger
- ☐ Heart
- ☐ Horseshoe
- ☐ Hot dog
- ☐ Locker
- ☐ Lost sneaker
- ☐ Mask
- ☐ Mummy
- ☐ Pencil
- ☐ Snowman
- ☐ Straw
- ☐ Telescope
- ☐ Trophy
- ☐ Turtle
- ☐ Water bucket
- ☐ Whistle
- ☐ Worm

What is a punt?
What is a player's shirt called?

OFFENSE:
C – CENTER
G – GUARD
WR – WIDE RECEIVER
T – TACKLE
TE – TIGHT END
QB – QUARTERBACK
B – BACK
DEFENSE:
DT – DEFENSIVE TACKLE
DE – DEFENSIVE END
LB – LINEBACKER
DB – DEFENSIVE BACK
FS – FREE SAFETY
SS – STRONG SAFETY
NT – NOSE TACKLE

THE FIRST PRO GAME WAS PLAYED IN LATROBE, PA.

THE NFL (NATIONAL FOOTBALL LEAGUE) WAS FORMED IN 1922.

THERE ARE 32 TEAMS IN THE NFL. THE CHAMPIONSHIP IS CALLED THE SUPER BOWL.

THE FIRST SUPER BOWL WAS PLAYED IN 1967. THE GREEN BAY PACKERS BEAT THE KANSAS CITY CHIEFS, 35-10.

THE FIELD IS 100 YARDS LONG AND 160 FEET WIDE. THE FIELD IS ALSO CALLED THE GRIDIRON.

WHITE LINES, CALLED YARDLINES, RUN ACROSS THE FIELD EVERY FIVE YARDS.

HURRY UP WITH THAT BALL!

TWO ROWS OF SHORT WHITE LINES, CALLED HASH MARKS, SET ONE YARD APART, ALSO RUN THE LENGTH OF FIELD. ALL PLAYS BEGIN WITH THE BALL ON OR BETWEEN THE HASH MARKS.

GOAL POST

END ZONE

50 YD. LINE

COACH

END ZONE

GOAL POST

THE AIR-FILLED LEATHER BALL WEIGHS 14-15 OUNCES AND IS ABOUT 11 INCHES FROM POINT TO POINT.

THE LACES PROVIDE A GOOD GRIP FOR PASSERS AND BALL CARRIERS.

CARRYING OR PASSING THE BALL INTO THE OPPONENTS END ZONE IS A TOUCHDOWN... GOOD FOR 6 POINTS. AN EXTRA POINT CAN THEN BE MADE BY KICKING THE BALL THROUGH THE GOAL POSTS.

OTHER POINTS: FIELD GOAL – 3 POINTS. OCCURS WHEN THE BALL IS KICKED THROUGH THE OTHER TEAM'S GOAL POST. SAFETY – 2 POINTS. OCCURS WHEN A PLAYER WITH THE BALL IS TACKLED IN HIS OWN END ZONE.

HOT DOGS

WR

THE STANLEY CUP IS THE CHAMPIONSHIP TROPHY OF THE NATIONAL HOCKEY LEAGUE.

IT WAS DONATED BY FREDERICK ARTHUR, LORD STANLEY OF PRESTON, IN 1893.

HE WAS GOVERNOR-GENERAL OF CANADA.

THE STANLEY CUP PLAYOFFS HAVE BEEN HELD SINCE 1894.

EACH TEAM HAS NO MORE THAN SIX PLAYERS ON THE ICE AT ONE TIME.

A REFEREE AND TWO LINESMEN CONTROL EACH GAME.

YOU ARE IN THE CENTER ZONE.

THE MONTREAL CANADIENS HAVE WON THE STANLEY CUP A RECORD 23 TIMES.

•STANDARD RING SIZE• 200 FEET LONG 85 FEET WIDE

CENTER → LINE OR RED LINE

THERE ARE 30 PROFESSIONAL TEAMS IN THE NATIONAL HOCKEY LEAGUE.

YOU ARE IN THE END ZONE.

BLUE LINE

VERY THIN ICE

I'M THE GOALKEEPER OR GOALIE. I DEFEND MY TEAM'S NET.

GOALIES ARE THE ONLY PLAYERS ALLOWED TO CATCH THE PUCK OR PICK IT UP.

IN 1928-1929, MONTREAL GOALIE GEORGE HAINSWORTH HAD 22 SHUTOUTS IN 44 GAMES.

I'M THE REFEREE.

THIS IS MY KIND OF TEAM!

MOST HOCKEY GAMES ARE PLAYED IN THREE TWENTY-MINUTE PERIODS.

ICE HOCKEY

Ice hockey's fast skating, rough checking, lightning-fast slapshots, and acrobatic saves make it an exciting sport. Ice hockey, an offshoot of field hockey, began in Canada in the 1800s.

At the end of every National League Hockey season, a silver trophy—the Stanley Cup—is awarded to the team that wins the championship game.

LEARN ABOUT ICE HOCKEY AS YOU LOOK FOR THESE FUN ITEMS:

❑ Baby's block	❑ Clown	❑ Heart	❑ Paper airplane	❑ Skunk
❑ Basketball	❑ Crown	❑ Hot dog	❑ Pencil	❑ Snowman
❑ Blackboard	❑ Feather	❑ Mouse	❑ Periscope	❑ Teapot
❑ Cactus	❑ Flower	❑ Paintbrush	❑ Ski	

What is a hat trick?
How many pro teams are there?

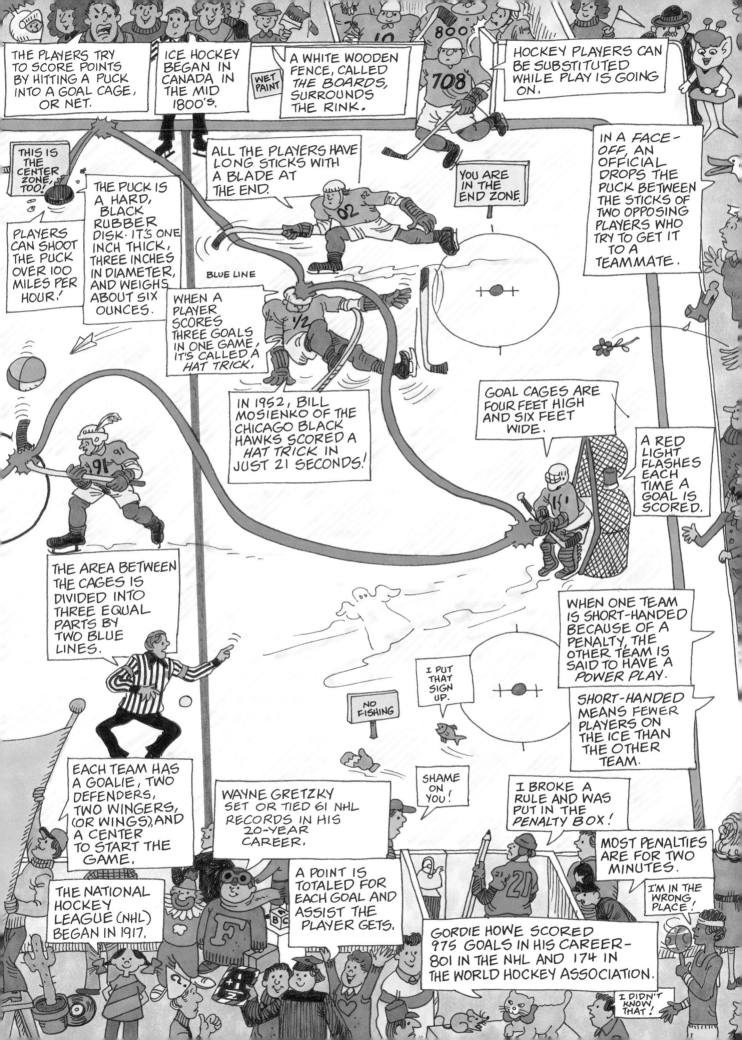

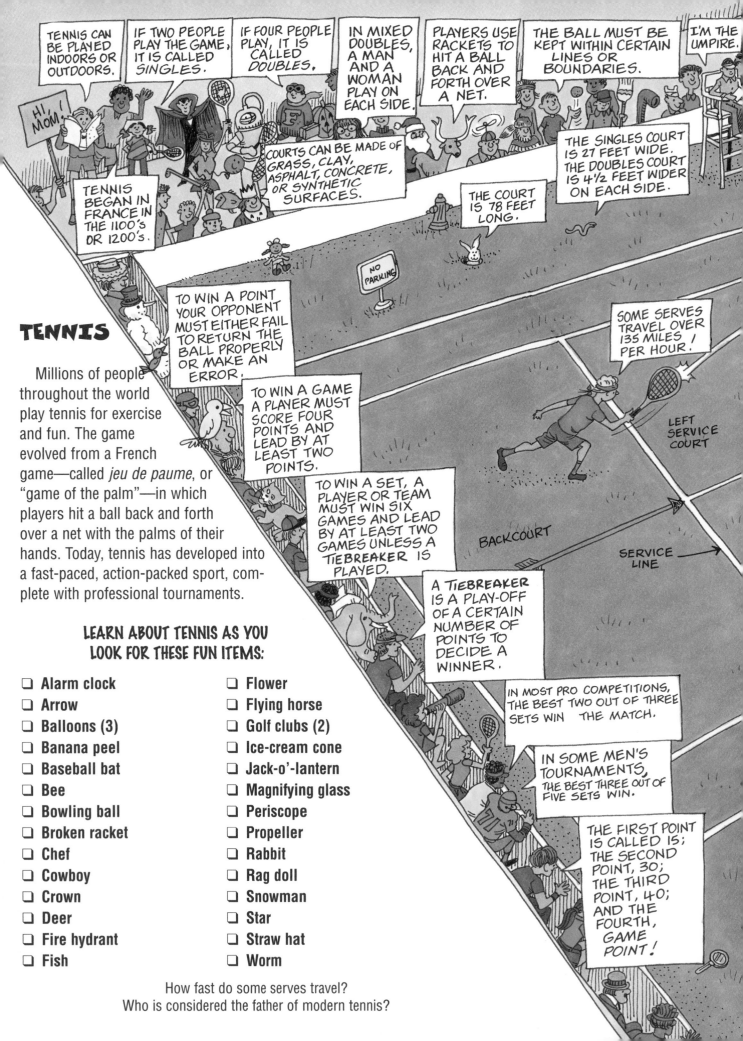

TENNIS

Millions of people throughout the world play tennis for exercise and fun. The game evolved from a French game—called *jeu de paume*, or "game of the palm"—in which players hit a ball back and forth over a net with the palms of their hands. Today, tennis has developed into a fast-paced, action-packed sport, complete with professional tournaments.

LEARN ABOUT TENNIS AS YOU LOOK FOR THESE FUN ITEMS:

- ❑ Alarm clock
- ❑ Arrow
- ❑ Balloons (3)
- ❑ Banana peel
- ❑ Baseball bat
- ❑ Bee
- ❑ Bowling ball
- ❑ Broken racket
- ❑ Chef
- ❑ Cowboy
- ❑ Crown
- ❑ Deer
- ❑ Fire hydrant
- ❑ Fish
- ❑ Flower
- ❑ Flying horse
- ❑ Golf clubs (2)
- ❑ Ice-cream cone
- ❑ Jack-o'-lantern
- ❑ Magnifying glass
- ❑ Periscope
- ❑ Propeller
- ❑ Rabbit
- ❑ Rag doll
- ❑ Snowman
- ❑ Star
- ❑ Straw hat
- ❑ Worm

How fast do some serves travel?
Who is considered the father of modern tennis?

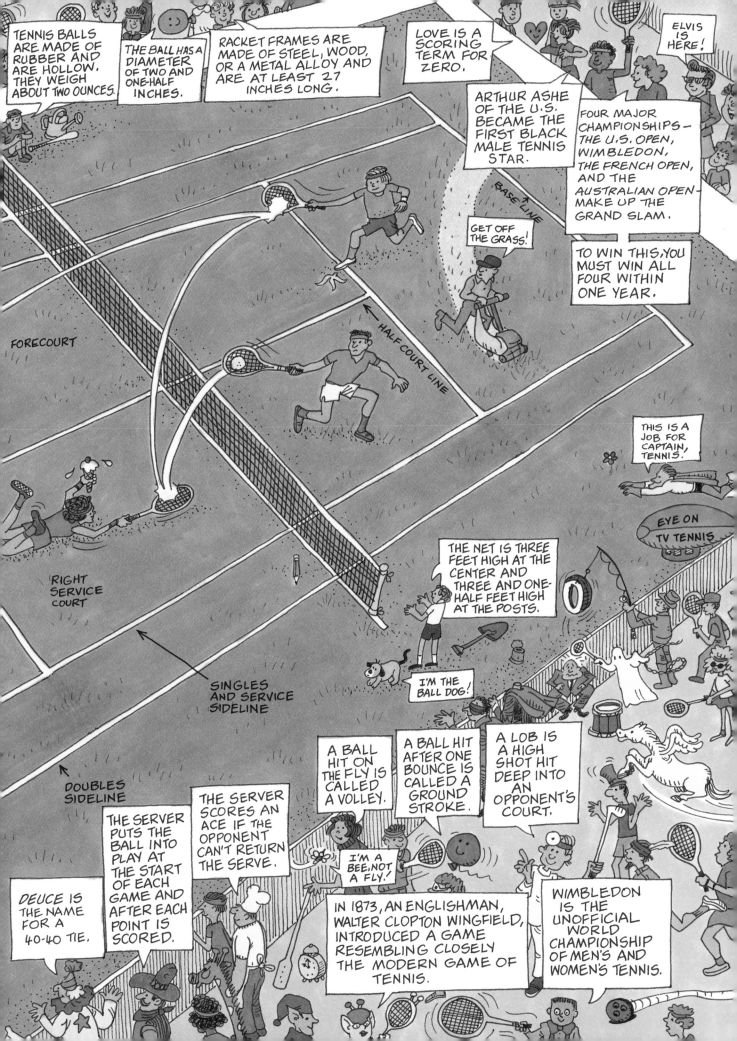

MARTIAL ARTS

The martial arts are more than a method of combat. They are important as a means of developing one's physical, spiritual, and mental well-being.

Centuries ago, Buddhist monks roamed throughout Asia, spreading their philosophy and knowledge of the martial arts. Each culture modified this philosophy to suit its needs, thus developing new martial arts techniques.

LEARN ABOUT MARTIAL ARTS AS YOU LOOK FOR THESE FUN ITEMS:

- ❑ Anchor
- ❑ Artist
- ❑ Banana peel
- ❑ Bird
- ❑ Black-belt ghost
- ❑ Bone
- ❑ Book
- ❑ Boxer
- ❑ Carrot
- ❑ Cat
- ❑ Chef's hat
- ❑ Clown
- ❑ Crown
- ❑ Football
- ❑ Jack-o'-lantern
- ❑ Karate rat
- ❑ Lost boot
- ❑ Lost glove
- ❑ Lost mitten
- ❑ Magnet
- ❑ Mummy
- ❑ Piggy bank
- ❑ Saw
- ❑ Scarecrow
- ❑ Skateboard
- ❑ Snake
- ❑ Speaker
- ❑ Stopwatch
- ❑ Wizard
- ❑ Yo-yo

What is tae kwon do? How do karate students toughen their hands and feet?

KARATE IS A FORM OF UNARMED COMBAT IN WHICH A PERSON KICKS OR STRIKES WITH HANDS, ELBOWS, FEET, OR KNEES.

THERE ARE FOUR MAJOR TYPES OF KARATE — CHINESE, JAPANESE, KOREAN, AND OKINAWAN.

THE JAPANESE WORD FOR KARATE MEANS EMPTY HAND TAKEN FROM "KARA," EMPTY, AND "TE," HAND.

TAE KWON DO IS THE KOREAN ART OF SELF-DEFENSE. IT EMPHASIZES KICKING. IT MEANS "FOOT-HAND ART."

TAE KWON DO COMBINES PHYSICAL AND MENTAL DISCIPLINE WITH A DEEP PHILOSOPHY.

IT'S AN OLYMPIC SPORT AND HAS BEEN PRACTICED FOR OVER 2,000 YEARS.

FOUR JUDGES-ONE SEATED AT EACH CORNER

I'M KARATE RAT.

- ·ARBITRATOR
- ·TIMEKEEPER
- ·RECORDKEEPER
- ·ADMINISTRATOR

STARTING LINE

REFEREE

STARTING LINE

STUDENTS TOUGHEN THEIR HANDS AND FEET BY POUNDING PADDED BOARDS.

CHINESE KARATE IS CALLED KUNG FU.

IT USES FLOWING, CIRCULAR MOTIONS.

THE BELT DENOTES THE WEARER'S RANK.

BEGINNERS WEAR WHITE.

EXPERTS WEAR BLACK.

OTHER COLORS DENOTE INTERMEDIATE RANKS.

THE UNIFORM IS CALLED GI.

MY PANTS SPLIT!

I HAVE A BLACK BELT.

TRACK AND FIELD

Track and field is a sport in which men and women compete in athletic events that feature running, throwing, and jumping. Track events consist of a series of races over various distances, ranging from 60 meters (65.6 yards) to a marathon. Field events measure an athlete's ability to throw or jump.

LEARN ABOUT TRACK AND FIELD AS YOU LOOK FOR THESE FUN ITEMS:

- ☐ Balloon
- ☐ Bee
- ☐ Birdcage
- ☐ Chef's hat
- ☐ Count Dracula
- ☐ Duck
- ☐ Elephant
- ☐ Fish
- ☐ Flying bat
- ☐ Football player
- ☐ Helicopter
- ☐ Ice-cream cone
- ☐ Mummy
- ☐ Ostrich
- ☐ Painted egg
- ☐ Periscope
- ☐ Pig
- ☐ Pizza deliveryman
- ☐ Rabbit
- ☐ Roller skater
- ☐ Surfboard
- ☐ Tuba
- ☐ Turtle
- ☐ Umbrella

How long is a marathon?
Name the four throwing events.

TRACK EVENTS CONSIST OF RACES OVER VARIOUS DISTANCES.

FIELD EVENTS TEST THE ATHLETE'S SKILL AT JUMPING AND THROWING.

ALL RACES UP TO 400 METERS OR 440 YARDS ARE CALLED SPRINTS OR DASHES.

RAYMOND CLARENCE EWRY, OF THE U.S., WON A TOTAL OF 10 GOLD MEDALS IN THE 1900, 1904, 1906, AND 1908 OLYMPICS.

IN 1988, FLORENCE JOYNER GRIFFITH SET THE WOMEN'S RECORD FOR THE 100-METER DASH: 10.49 SECONDS.

TV COVERAGE

IN 1954, ROGER BANNISTER OF GREAT BRITAIN WAS THE FIRST RUNNER TO BREAK THE 4-MINUTE MILE RECORD.

TRACK AND FIELD IS HELD OUTDOORS AND INDOORS. SEPARATE RECORDS ARE KEPT FOR EACH.

PAAVO NURMI OF FINLAND WON FOUR OLYMPIC GOLD MEDALS IN 1924. HE FINISHED HIS CAREER WITH 12 MEDALS (NINE GOLD AND THREE SILVER).

I'M A TRACK AND FIELD STAR.

NO. 1

JESSE OWENS SET SIX WORLD RECORDS IN 45 MINUTES, IN 1935. THE EVENTS WERE: 100-YARD DASH, LONG JUMP, 200-METER DASH, 220-YARD AND 200-METER LOW HURDLES.

SHOT PUT AREA

DISCUS AREA

THE DECATHLON IS MADE UP OF 10 EVENTS. THEY ARE ...

OVAL TRACK

HIGH-JUMP AREA

SAND PIT

FOAM RUBBER PIT

LONG-JUMP AREA

JAVELIN AREA

THE ATHLETES RACE ON AN OVAL TRACK.

MOST OUTDOOR TRACKS ARE 1/4 MILE OR 400 METERS LONG.

EXTREME SPORTS

What's more fun than taking action to the edge? "Nothing!" say extreme-sports fans.

LEARN ABOUT BMX AS YOU LOOK FOR THESE FUN ITEMS:

- [ ] Brush
- [ ] Flower
- [ ] Football
- [ ] Key
- [ ] Paintbrush
- [ ] Snail
- [ ] Star
- [ ] Worms (2)

LEARN ABOUT SNOWBOARDING AS YOU LOOK FOR THESE FUN ITEMS:

- [ ] Baseball cap
- [ ] Birds (2)
- [ ] Cactus
- [ ] Heart
- [ ] Lost cap
- [ ] Rabbit
- [ ] Sled
- [ ] Star
- [ ] Sunglasses

LEARN ABOUT SKATEBOARDING AS YOU LOOK FOR THESE FUN ITEMS:

- [ ] Balloons
- [ ] Elephant
- [ ] Half moon
- [ ] Kite
- [ ] Lightning bolts (2)
- [ ] Stars (3)
- [ ] Top hat

What does *BMX* stand for?
Who invented the snowboard?
What is an Ollie?

FAMOUS PEOPLE AND PLACES

WALT DISNEY WORLD

Walt Disney World is the fulfillment of Walt Disney's dream. He wanted to create the ultimate amusement park, which adults and children could enjoy together. Today, Walt Disney World in Florida is the most popular man-made attraction in the world, visited by thousands of people each day.

LEARN ABOUT WALT DISNEY WORLD AS YOU LOOK FOR THESE FUN ITEMS:

- ☐ Arrow
- ☐ Balloon
- ☐ Cake
- ☐ Chef's hat
- ☐ Clown
- ☐ Elephants (2)
- ☐ Fish
- ☐ Football
- ☐ Ghost
- ☐ Hearts (3)
- ☐ Horse
- ☐ Ice-cream cone
- ☐ Kite
- ☐ Ladder
- ☐ Magnifying glass
- ☐ Penguin
- ☐ Snowman
- ☐ TV set

Who starred in *Steamboat Willie*?
On what day is Walt Disney World busiest?

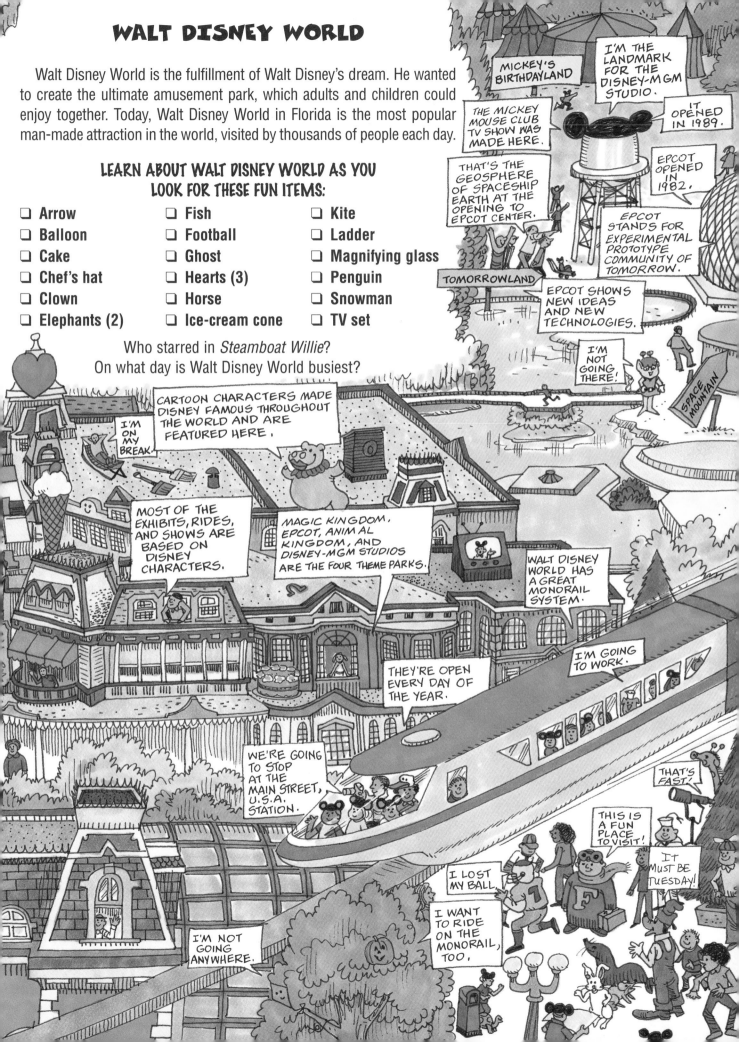

SACAGAWEA

Sacagawea *(SAK-uh-juh-WEE-uh)* was born among the Shoshone *(shoh-SHOH-nee)* Indians. As a young girl, she was captured by an enemy tribe, then sold as a slave to a French-Canadian trader, who later married her. Sacagawea and her husband both joined the expedition led by Meriwether Lewis and William Clark in 1804-1805. Sacagawea served as interpreter and guide as the team crossed western lands to the Pacific Ocean, then back again.

LEARN ABOUT SACAGAWEA AS YOU LOOK FOR THESE FUN ITEMS:

- ❑ Armadillo
- ❑ Arrows (2)
- ❑ Bears (2)
- ❑ Beaver
- ❑ Bow
- ❑ Buffalo
- ❑ Deer
- ❑ Drum
- ❑ Eagle
- ❑ Egg
- ❑ Flying bat
- ❑ Flying saucer
- ❑ Frog
- ❑ Groundhog
- ❑ Heart
- ❑ Lost boot
- ❑ Moose
- ❑ Mushroom
- ❑ Owl
- ❑ Rabbits (3)
- ❑ Sailboat
- ❑ Skunk
- ❑ Snake
- ❑ Spear
- ❑ Wild turkey

What does *Sacagawea* mean? Why did she agree to guide Lewis and Clark?

NEIL ARMSTRONG

Neil Alden Armstrong is one of the most famous U.S. astronauts. On July 20, 1969, Armstrong and fellow astronaut Edwin "Buzz" Aldrin Jr. landed the *Eagle*—*Apollo 11*'s lunar module—on the moon's surface. Armstrong became the first person to set foot on the moon.

LEARN ABOUT NEIL ARMSTRONG AS YOU LOOK FOR THESE FUN ITEMS:

- ☐ Balloon
- ☐ Banana peel
- ☐ Bird
- ☐ Cactus
- ☐ Can
- ☐ Cloud
- ☐ Firecracker
- ☐ Fire hydrant
- ☐ Fish (3)
- ☐ Flashlight
- ☐ Flying saucer
- ☐ Heart
- ☐ Hot-air balloon
- ☐ Hot dog
- ☐ Ice-cream cone
- ☐ Key
- ☐ Kite
- ☐ Lamp
- ☐ Mouse
- ☐ Paper airplane
- ☐ Pencil
- ☐ Police officer
- ☐ School bus
- ☐ Sock
- ☐ Superhero
- ☐ Top hat
- ☐ Umbrella
- ☐ Wagon wheel

What did Neil Armstrong say when he first set foot on the moon's surface?
About how much would you weigh on the moon?

WASHINGTON, D.C.

George Washington envisioned a city of beauty and stature to serve as the nation's capital. In 1791, he hired Pierre L'Enfant—a French architect and engineer—to design it. L'Enfant's plan served Washington's dream well. The city has wide, straight avenues; lush parks; towering monuments; and beautiful trees and flowers. It also is an important political center, where decisions affecting millions of lives are made daily at the White House (home of the president), the Capitol (home of the U.S. Congress), the Supreme Court, and many federal agencies.

LEARN ABOUT WASHINGTON, D.C., AS YOU LOOK FOR THESE FUN ITEMS:

- ❑ Balloon
- ❑ Baseball cap
- ❑ Bird
- ❑ Cactus
- ❑ Fish
- ❑ Fishbowl
- ❑ Flags (3)
- ❑ Flower
- ❑ Headband
- ❑ Key
- ❑ Kite
- ❑ Mouse
- ❑ Paintbrush
- ❑ Scarves (2)
- ❑ Star
- ❑ Top hat
- ❑ Turtle

What is this city's purpose?

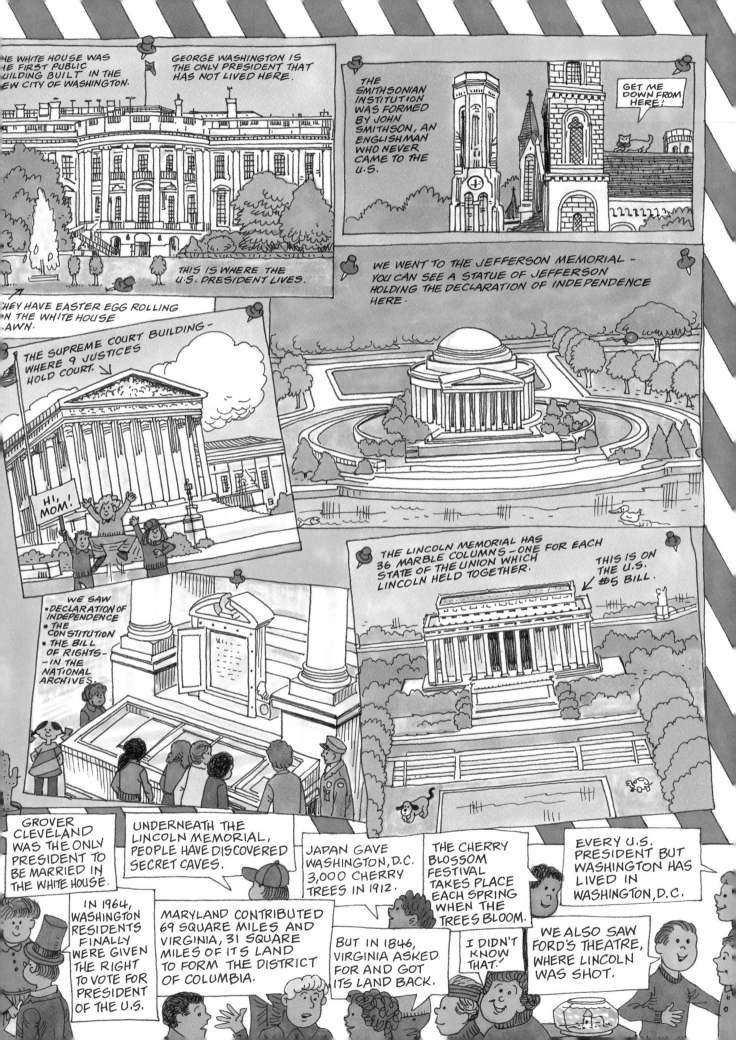

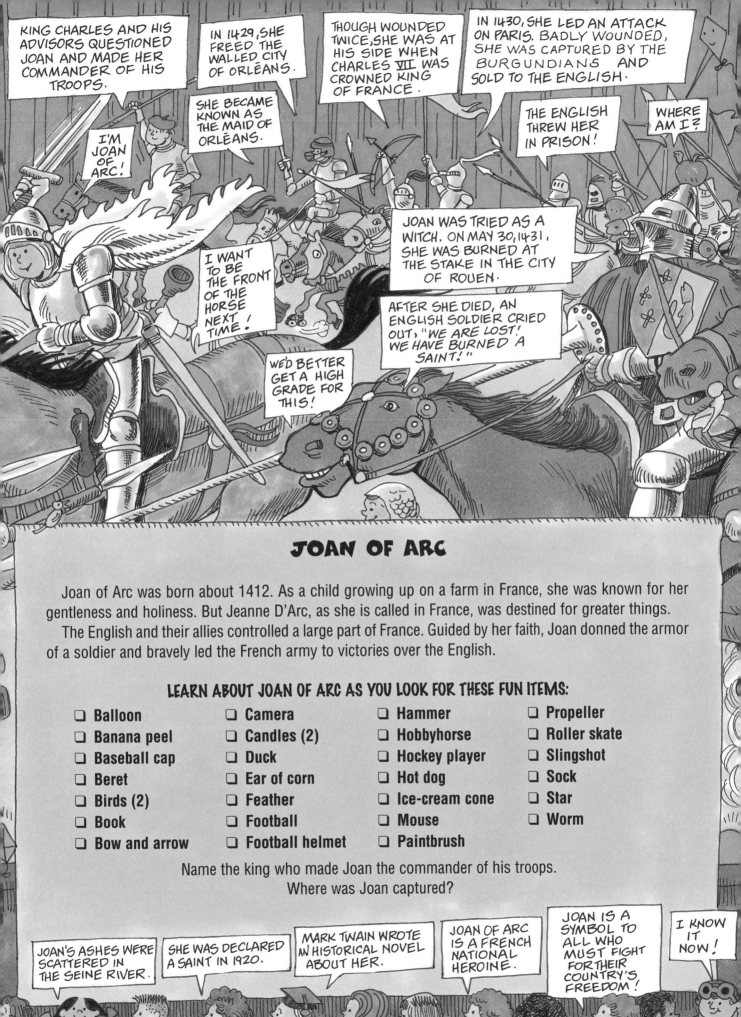

JOAN OF ARC

Joan of Arc was born about 1412. As a child growing up on a farm in France, she was known for her gentleness and holiness. But Jeanne D'Arc, as she is called in France, was destined for greater things.

The English and their allies controlled a large part of France. Guided by her faith, Joan donned the armor of a soldier and bravely led the French army to victories over the English.

LEARN ABOUT JOAN OF ARC AS YOU LOOK FOR THESE FUN ITEMS:

- ❏ Balloon
- ❏ Banana peel
- ❏ Baseball cap
- ❏ Beret
- ❏ Birds (2)
- ❏ Book
- ❏ Bow and arrow
- ❏ Camera
- ❏ Candles (2)
- ❏ Duck
- ❏ Ear of corn
- ❏ Feather
- ❏ Football
- ❏ Football helmet
- ❏ Hammer
- ❏ Hobbyhorse
- ❏ Hockey player
- ❏ Hot dog
- ❏ Ice-cream cone
- ❏ Mouse
- ❏ Paintbrush
- ❏ Propeller
- ❏ Roller skate
- ❏ Slingshot
- ❏ Sock
- ❏ Star
- ❏ Worm

Name the king who made Joan the commander of his troops.
Where was Joan captured?

JACQUES-YVES COUSTEAU

Jacques-Yves Cousteau made scuba diving and underwater exploration popular by inventing and perfecting the aqualung. Cousteau won many awards for his underwater films, and also wrote many books about sea life. He began the Cousteau Society to preserve the beauty of the ocean life he loved to explore.

LEARN ABOUT JACQUES-YVES COUSTEAU AS YOU LOOK FOR THESE FUN ITEMS:

- ❑ Balloons (3)
- ❑ Bathyscaphe
- ❑ Bottle
- ❑ Bucket
- ❑ Can
- ❑ Duck
- ❑ Hammer
- ❑ Helicopter
- ❑ Horseshoe
- ❑ Horseshoe crab
- ❑ Jellyfish
- ❑ Lifesaver
- ❑ Lost oar
- ❑ Lost shorts
- ❑ Palm tree
- ❑ Paper airplane
- ❑ Pencil
- ❑ Periscope
- ❑ Sailboat
- ❑ Sea horse
- ❑ Shipwreck
- ❑ Shipwrecked sailor
- ❑ Starfish
- ❑ Surfer
- ❑ Swan
- ❑ Telescope
- ❑ Tire
- ❑ TV set
- ❑ Wagon wheel

What was the name of Cousteau's research ship?
What did Cousteau help invent that is used by scuba divers?

NEW YORK CITY

New York City is the most populous city in the United States. It is a universal center for art, fashion, architecture, finance, publishing, and more. A great deal of what happens in New York affects what happens around the country and even around the world.

LEARN ABOUT NEW YORK CITY AS YOU LOOK FOR THESE FUN ITEMS:

- ❑ Apple
- ❑ Baseball
- ❑ Bird
- ❑ Blimp
- ❑ Book
- ❑ Boom box
- ❑ Container ship
- ❑ Diver
- ❑ Ferry
- ❑ Fish
- ❑ Flower
- ❑ Flying saucer
- ❑ Football
- ❑ Ghost
- ❑ Heart
- ❑ Helicopter
- ❑ Periscope
- ❑ Rowboat
- ❑ Star
- ❑ Telescope
- ❑ Tire
- ❑ Top hat
- ❑ Tugboat
- ❑ Worm

Who first settled New York?
When was it the nation's capital?

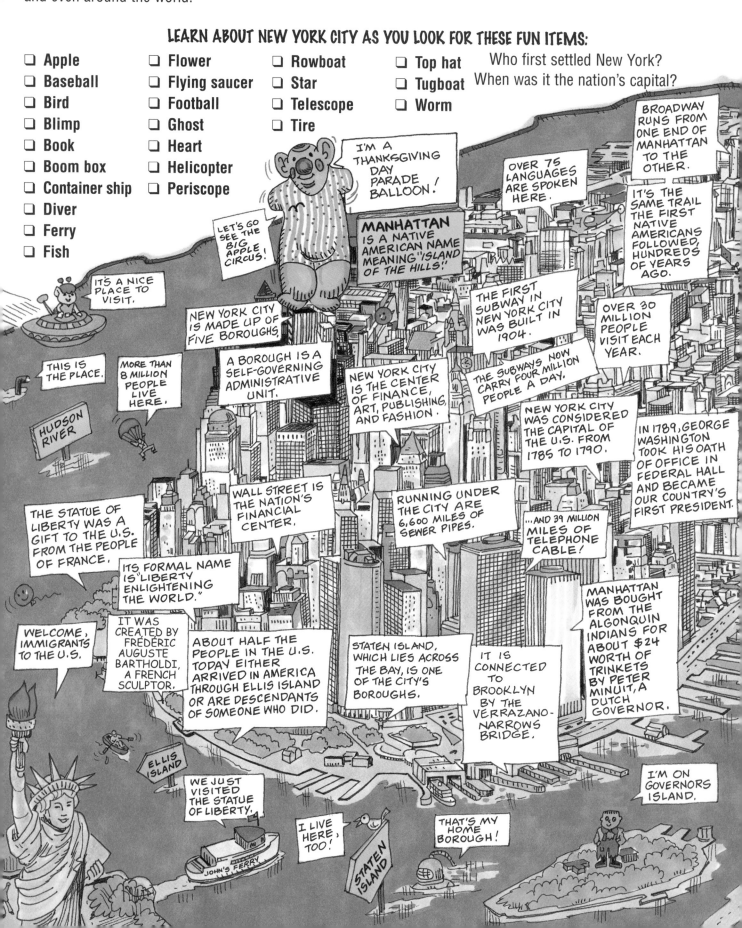

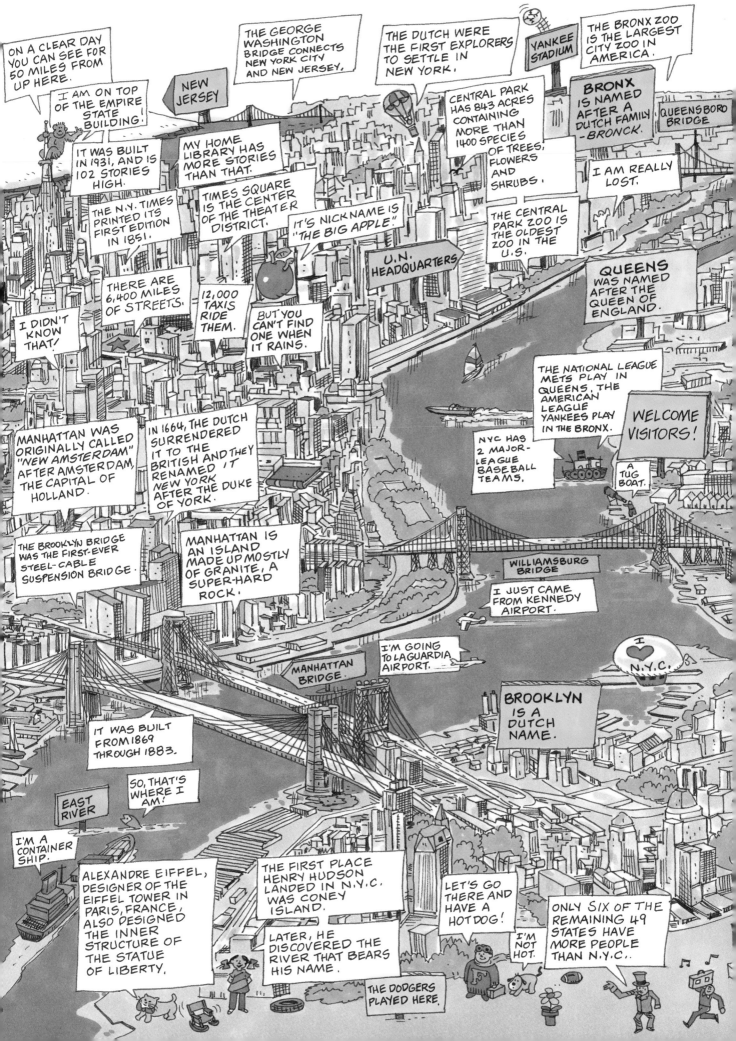

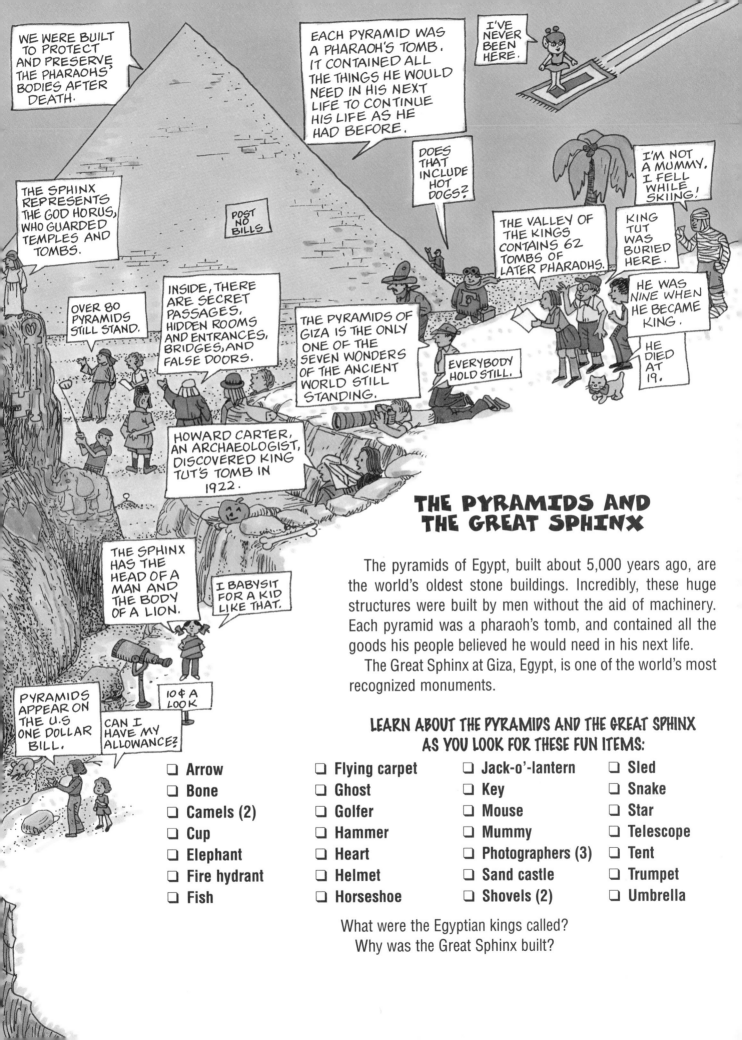

THE PYRAMIDS AND THE GREAT SPHINX

The pyramids of Egypt, built about 5,000 years ago, are the world's oldest stone buildings. Incredibly, these huge structures were built by men without the aid of machinery. Each pyramid was a pharaoh's tomb, and contained all the goods his people believed he would need in his next life.

The Great Sphinx at Giza, Egypt, is one of the world's most recognized monuments.

LEARN ABOUT THE PYRAMIDS AND THE GREAT SPHINX AS YOU LOOK FOR THESE FUN ITEMS:

- ❏ Arrow
- ❏ Bone
- ❏ Camels (2)
- ❏ Cup
- ❏ Elephant
- ❏ Fire hydrant
- ❏ Fish
- ❏ Flying carpet
- ❏ Ghost
- ❏ Golfer
- ❏ Hammer
- ❏ Heart
- ❏ Helmet
- ❏ Horseshoe
- ❏ Jack-o'-lantern
- ❏ Key
- ❏ Mouse
- ❏ Mummy
- ❏ Photographers (3)
- ❏ Sand castle
- ❏ Shovels (2)
- ❏ Sled
- ❏ Snake
- ❏ Star
- ❏ Telescope
- ❏ Tent
- ❏ Trumpet
- ❏ Umbrella

What were the Egyptian kings called?
Why was the Great Sphinx built?

LEONARDO DA VINCI

Leonardo da Vinci (1452–1519) was one of the greatest artists of the Renaissance. However, his interests and accomplishments went far beyond the world of art. He was, at various times, an inventor, scientist, engineer, architect, and designer. Leonardo's investigations marked the beginning of the scientific revolution and paved the way for scientists and inventors who followed him to take their places in history.

LEARN ABOUT LEONARDO DA VINCI AS YOU LOOK FOR THESE FUN ITEMS:

- ❑ Balloon
- ❑ Banana peel
- ❑ Birds (2)
- ❑ Bone
- ❑ Candles (13)
- ❑ Cane
- ❑ Chef
- ❑ Crown
- ❑ Doctor
- ❑ Duck
- ❑ Easel
- ❑ Feather
- ❑ Flowerpot
- ❑ Flying bat

- ❑ Ghost
- ❑ Graduate
- ❑ *La Gioconda*
- ❑ Ladder
- ❑ Lifesaver
- ❑ Lost shoe
- ❑ Mouse
- ❑ Paintbrushes (2)
- ❑ Paint bucket
- ❑ Painted egg
- ❑ Paper airplane
- ❑ Pencil
- ❑ Pizza
- ❑ Screwdriver

- ❑ Skull
- ❑ Snowman
- ❑ Stool
- ❑ Wizard

For what is the *Mona Lisa* famous?
Why must a mirror be used in order to read Leonardo's notebooks?

SKETCH FOR AN EQUESTRIAN STATUE

HUMAN PROPORTIONS RECONSTRUCTED ACCORDING TO VITRUVIUS — 1487-90

PLAN FOR A CHURCH — 1487-89

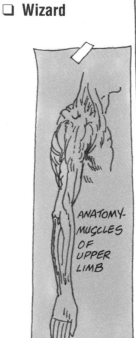

ANATOMY — MUSCLES OF UPPER LIMB

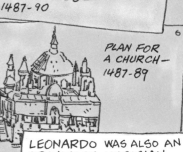

LEONARDO WAS ALSO AN ARCHITECT, MUSICIAN, MATHEMATICIAN, AND SCULPTOR.

HE'S GOING TO PAINT MY PORTRAIT.

"RENAISSANCE" MEANS "REBIRTH."

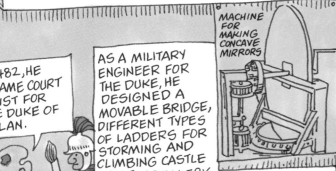

MACHINE FOR MAKING CONCAVE MIRRORS

WELL PUMP

IN 1482, HE BECAME COURT ARTIST FOR THE DUKE OF MILAN.

AS A MILITARY ENGINEER FOR THE DUKE, HE DESIGNED A MOVABLE BRIDGE, DIFFERENT TYPES OF LADDERS FOR STORMING AND CLIMBING CASTLE WALLS, ARTILLERY, AND GUNS.

HIS PAINTINGS ARE GRACEFUL, CALM, AND DELICATE.

HE EXPLORED HUMAN ANATOMY AND PERSPECTIVE.

ANATOMY IS THE STUDY OF THE STRUCTURE OF THE BODY.

HIS ARE THE FIRST ACCURATE DRAWINGS OF ANATOMY.

THE FIRST SUCCESSFUL HELICOPTER, DESIGNED IN THE 1930S, WAS BASED ON LEONARDO'S DRAWINGS.

HE BASED HIS DRAWINGS ON THE ACTION OF A SCREW.

HE HAS GREAT POWERS OF OBSERVATION.

HE RECORDED HIS IDEAS OF ART, SCIENCE, AND ENGINEERING IN NOTEBOOKS.

HE WROTE HIS NOTES BACKWARD SO THEY CAN ONLY BE READ USING A MIRROR.

I'M LOST!

HE MADE MAPS OF EUROPE.

YOU ARE HERE X

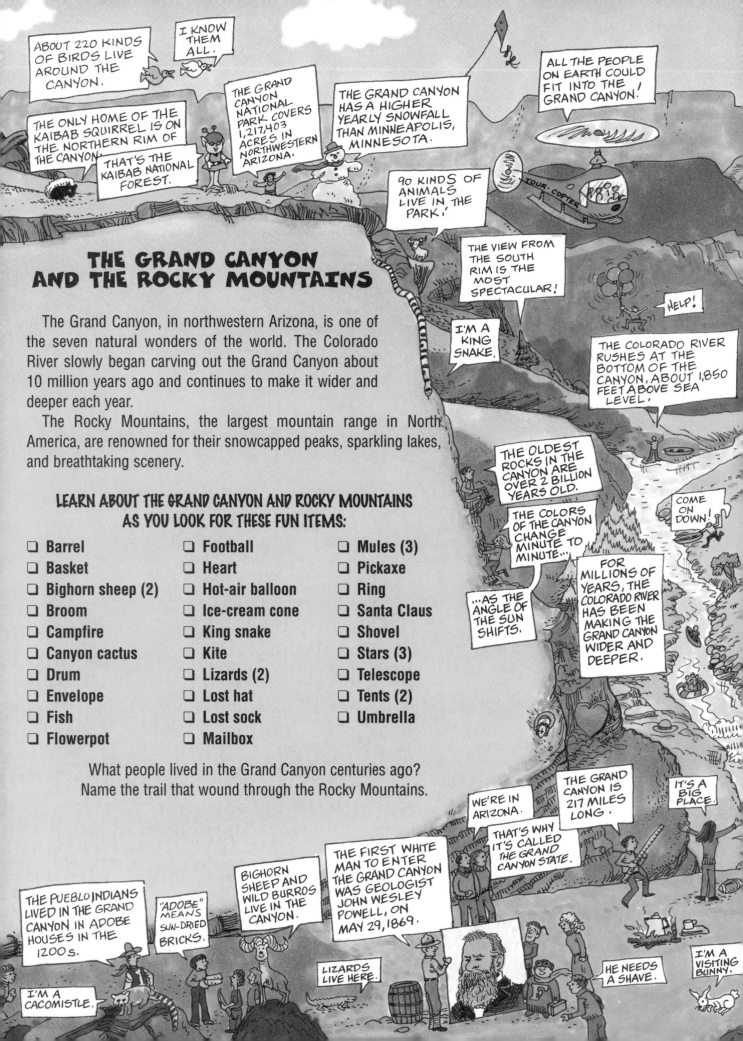

THE GRAND CANYON AND THE ROCKY MOUNTAINS

The Grand Canyon, in northwestern Arizona, is one of the seven natural wonders of the world. The Colorado River slowly began carving out the Grand Canyon about 10 million years ago and continues to make it wider and deeper each year.

The Rocky Mountains, the largest mountain range in North America, are renowned for their snowcapped peaks, sparkling lakes, and breathtaking scenery.

LEARN ABOUT THE GRAND CANYON AND ROCKY MOUNTAINS AS YOU LOOK FOR THESE FUN ITEMS:

- ❑ Barrel
- ❑ Basket
- ❑ Bighorn sheep (2)
- ❑ Broom
- ❑ Campfire
- ❑ Canyon cactus
- ❑ Drum
- ❑ Envelope
- ❑ Fish
- ❑ Flowerpot
- ❑ Football
- ❑ Heart
- ❑ Hot-air balloon
- ❑ Ice-cream cone
- ❑ King snake
- ❑ Kite
- ❑ Lizards (2)
- ❑ Lost hat
- ❑ Lost sock
- ❑ Mailbox
- ❑ Mules (3)
- ❑ Pickaxe
- ❑ Ring
- ❑ Santa Claus
- ❑ Shovel
- ❑ Stars (3)
- ❑ Telescope
- ❑ Tents (2)
- ❑ Umbrella

What people lived in the Grand Canyon centuries ago?
Name the trail that wound through the Rocky Mountains.

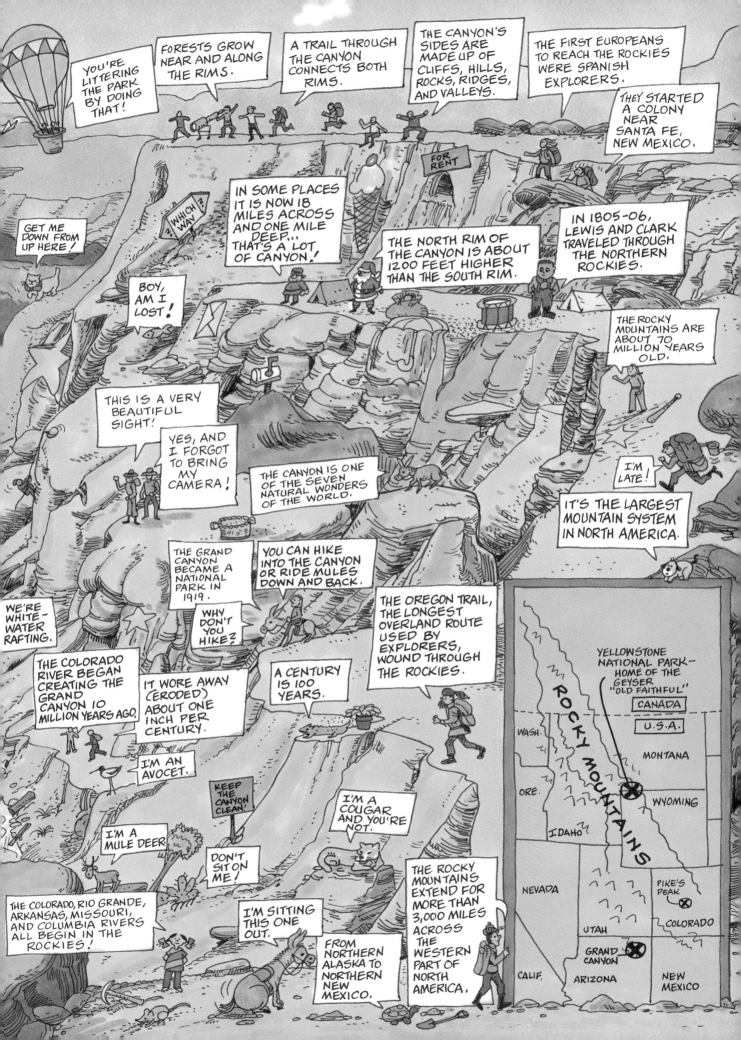

THE WORLD'S SEVEN CONTINENTS

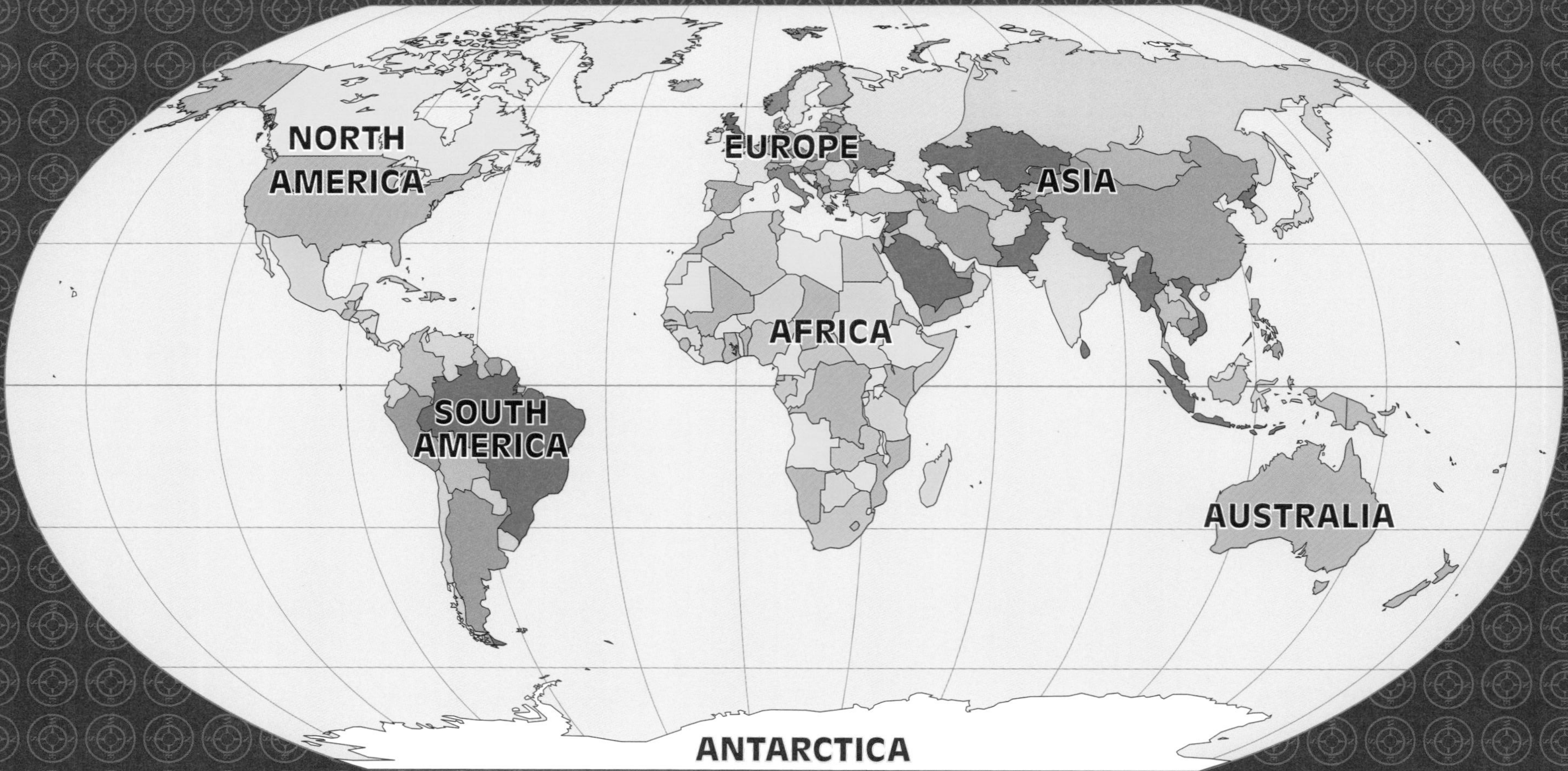

NORTH
AMERICA

SOUTH
AMERICA

EUROPE

AFRICA

ASIA

AUSTRALIA

ANTARCTICA

Populations are always changing. The populations listed in this book reflect generally accepted population numbers around the world as of 2008.

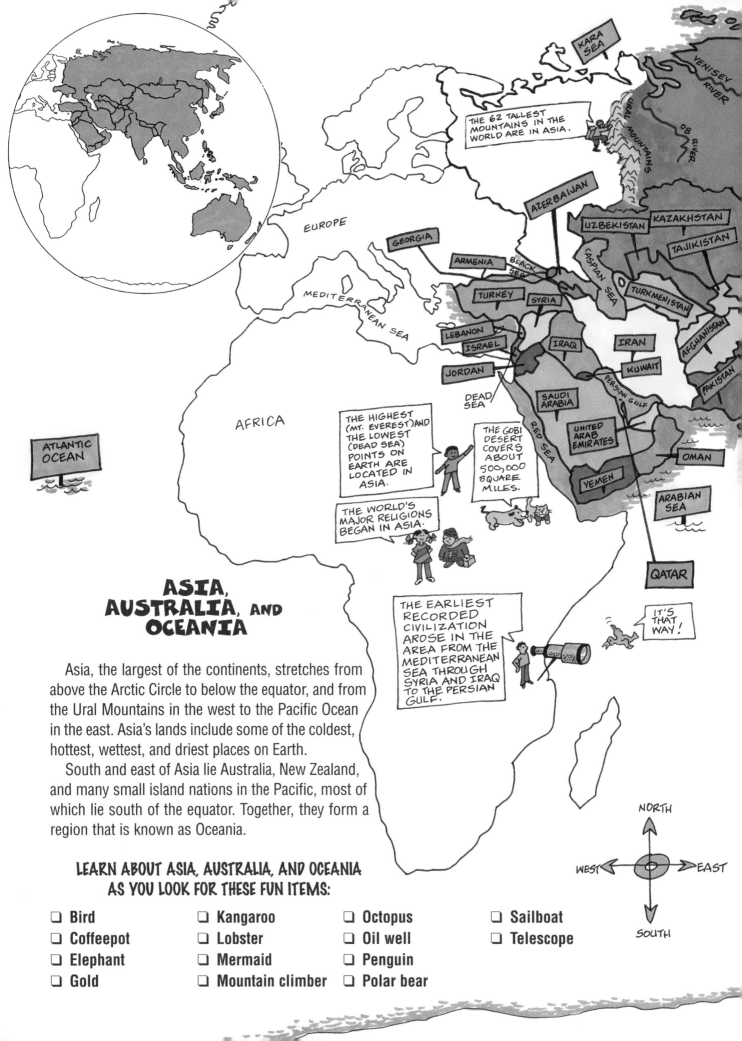

ASIA, AUSTRALIA, AND OCEANIA

Asia, the largest of the continents, stretches from above the Arctic Circle to below the equator, and from the Ural Mountains in the west to the Pacific Ocean in the east. Asia's lands include some of the coldest, hottest, wettest, and driest places on Earth.

South and east of Asia lie Australia, New Zealand, and many small island nations in the Pacific, most of which lie south of the equator. Together, they form a region that is known as Oceania.

LEARN ABOUT ASIA, AUSTRALIA, AND OCEANIA AS YOU LOOK FOR THESE FUN ITEMS:

- ❑ Bird
- ❑ Coffeepot
- ❑ Elephant
- ❑ Gold
- ❑ Kangaroo
- ❑ Lobster
- ❑ Mermaid
- ❑ Mountain climber
- ❑ Octopus
- ❑ Oil well
- ❑ Penguin
- ❑ Polar bear
- ❑ Sailboat
- ❑ Telescope

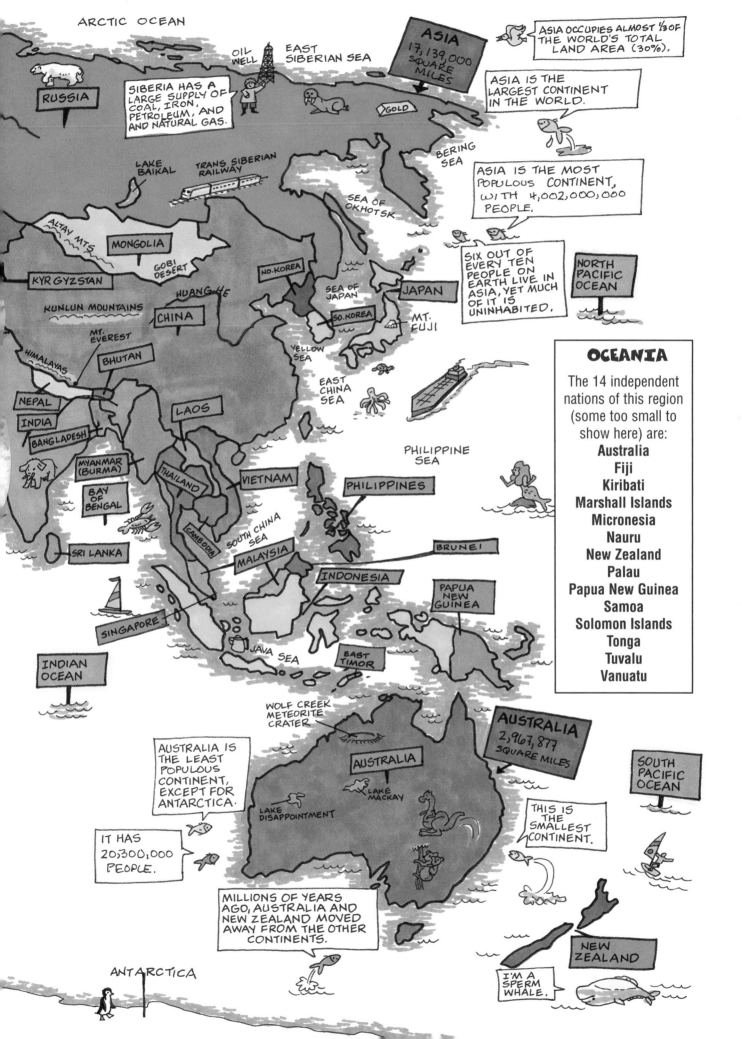

RUSSIA TAKES UP ONE SEVENTH OF THE WORLD'S TOTAL LAND AREA AND HAS THE EIGHTH LARGEST POPULATION.

TWO-THIRDS OF RUSSIA'S POPULATION LIVES IN EUROPE, WHILE ONLY A THIRD LIVES IN ASIA.

SNOW COVERS MORE THAN HALF OF RUSSIA FOR SIX MONTHS OF THE YEAR.

KARA SEA

BARENTS SEA

RUSSIA

FORESTS COVER MORE THAN HALF THE COUNTRY.

WHITE SEA

LAKE ONEGA

CARS AND TRACTORS MANUFACTURING

URAL MTS.

THE URAL MTS. DIVIDE RUSSIA BETWEEN EUROPE AND ASIA.

YENISEY RIVER

BALTIC SEA

LAKE LADOGA

ST. BASIL'S CATHEDRAL

GULF OF FINLAND

POTATOES

WHEAT

MOSCOW

OUR POPULATION IS 15,200,000.

OUR LANGUAGES ARE KAZAKH AND RUSSIAN.

BOLSHOI BALLET

THE REGION THAT LIES BETWEEN THE BLACK SEA AND THE CASPIAN SEA IS CALLED THE CAUCASUS.

OUR COUNTRY IS MAINLY STEPPE (A VAST SEMI-ARID PLAIN), DESERT, AND MOUNTAIN.

WE ARE ALMOST TWICE THE SIZE OF ALASKA.

GEORGIA'S POPULATION IS 4,650,000.

ITS WARM CLIMATE ATTRACTS TOURISTS.

KAZAKHSTAN

ALTAY MTS

ITS LANGUAGES ARE GEORGIAN, RUSSIAN, ARMENIAN, AND AZERI.

THE MAIN SPACE CENTER FOR THE COMMONWEALTH IS LOCATED HERE.

95% OF OUR COUNTRY IS MOUNTAINOUS.

TBILISI

OIL

CASPIAN SEA

UZBEKISTAN

ASTANA

BLACK SEA

TASHKENT

BISHKEK

KYRGYZSTAN

COMMUNISM PEAK (24,590 FT)

GEORGIA

ASHGABAT

90% IS COVERED BY KARA-KUM DESERT.

BAKU

ARMENIA

TAJIKISTAN

OUR POPULATION IS 7,300,000, AND OUR LANGUAGE IS TAJIK (ALSO RUSSIAN).

MEDITERRANEAN SEA

YEREVAN

AZERBAIJAN

TURKMENISTAN

DUSHANBE

THE LANGUAGES OF AZERBAIJAN ARE AZERI, RUSSIAN, AND ARMENIAN.

THEIR POPULATION IS 8,200,000.

ARMENIA IS THE MOST INDUSTRIALIZED STATE IN THE CAUCASUS.

TURKMENISTAN'S POPULATION IS 5,200,000, AND ITS LANGUAGES ARE TURKMEN, RUSSIAN, AND UZBEK.

ITS POPULATION IS 3,000,000.

MAIN LANGUAGES SPOKEN ARE ARMENIAN AND RUSSIAN.

RUSSIA AND ITS NEIGHBORS

Russia, the world's largest country, spans two continents. It covers more than 50 percent of Europe and more than 35 percent of Asia.

Russia used to be part of an even bigger nation called the Soviet Union, which broke apart in 1991. Many of the countries to Russia's south, now independent, also were part of the Soviet Union until 1991.

EUROPE

ASIA

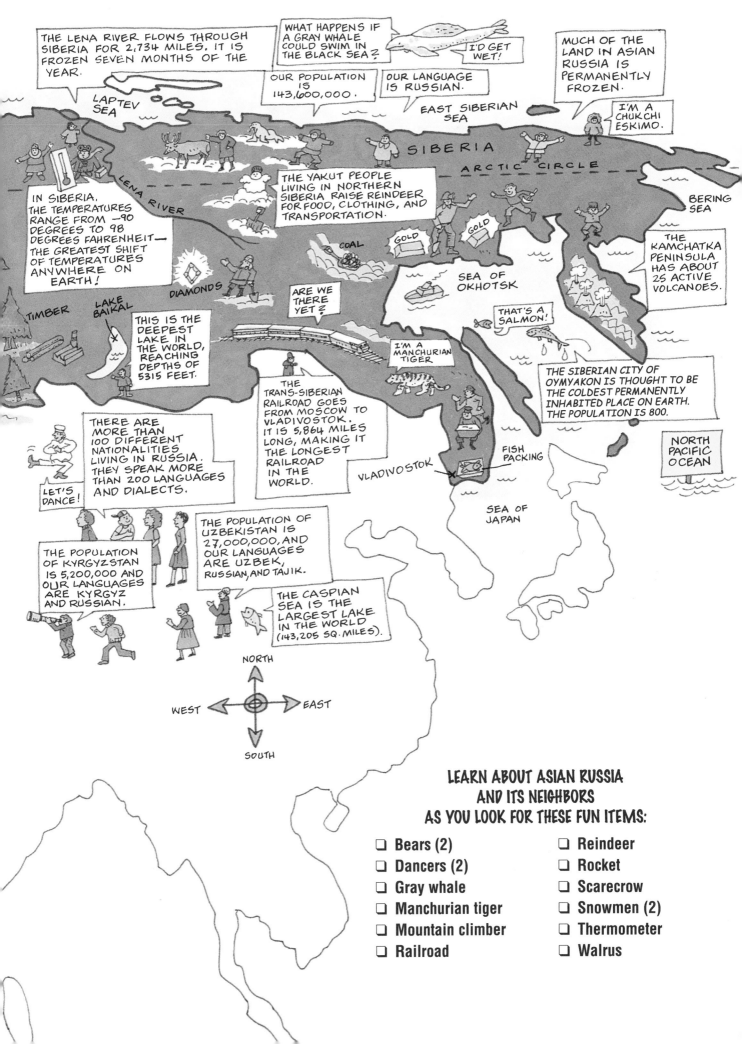

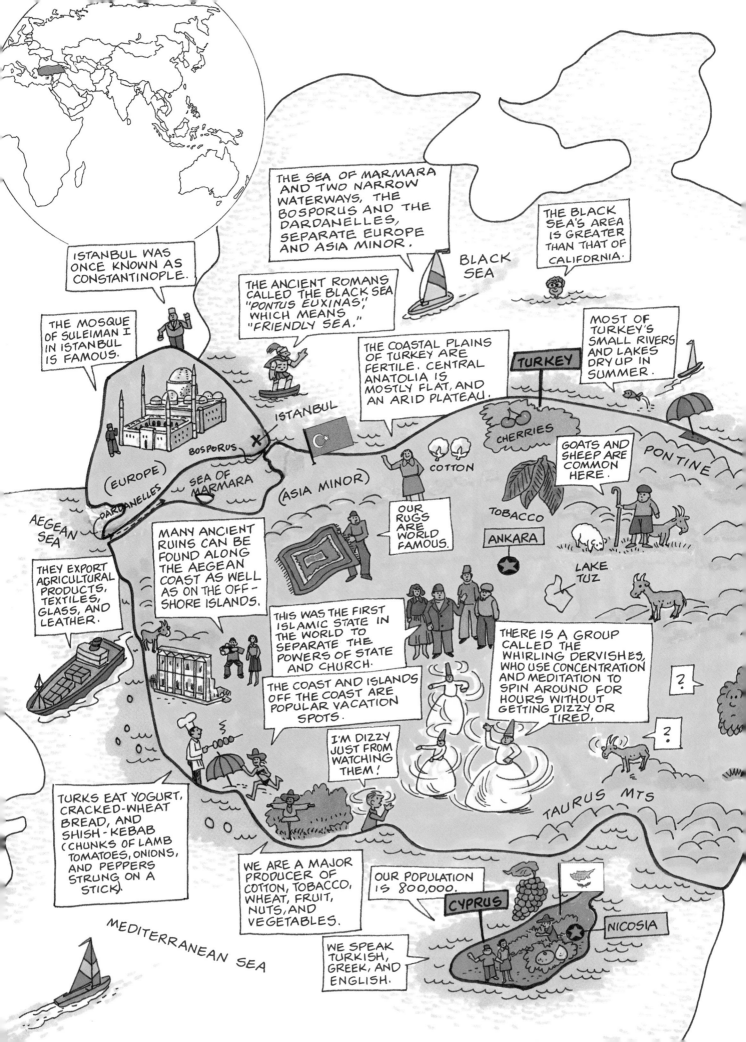

TURKEY and CYPRUS

Three percent of Turkey's land area lies in Europe. The rest is in Asia, in a region known as Anatolia or Asia Minor. Istanbul, which is Turkey's largest city, is the only city in the world that occupies land on two continents.

Cyprus is only 140 miles long at its longest point, and 60 miles wide at its widest point. It has long been controlled by other nations, and Greece and Turkey both still claim parts of it.

LEARN ABOUT TURKEY AND CYPRUS AS YOU LOOK FOR THESE FUN ITEMS:

- ❑ Apples
- ❑ Ball
- ❑ Bears (3)
- ❑ Book
- ❑ Cook
- ❑ Cowboy
- ❑ Egg
- ❑ Fish
- ❑ Goats (5)
- ❑ Grapes
- ❑ Ibis
- ❑ Ladder
- ❑ Sailboats (3)
- ❑ Shepherd
- ❑ Tea bag
- ❑ Telescope
- ❑ Tin Man
- ❑ Umbrellas (2)

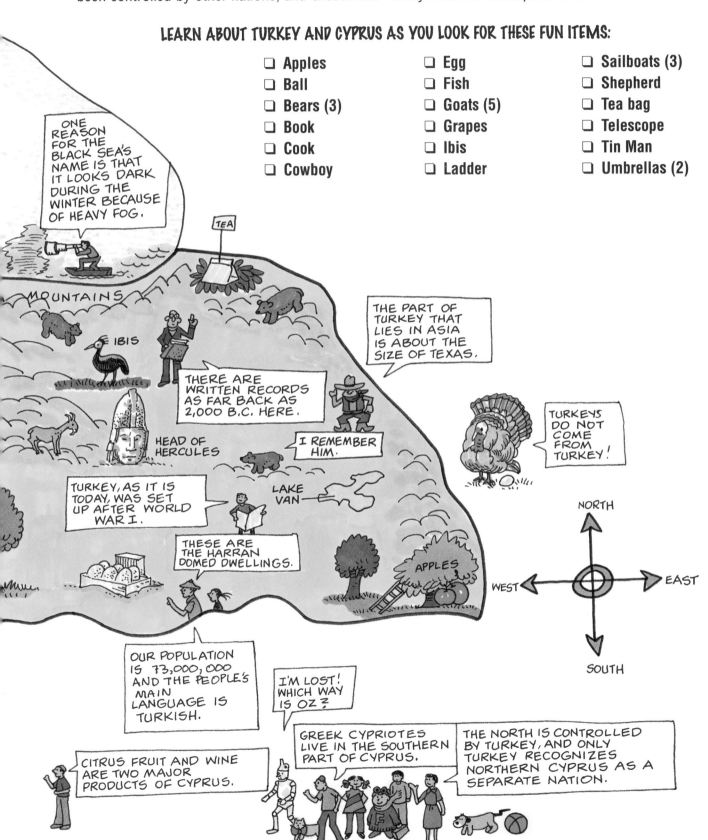

THE MIDDLE EAST

This part of Asia, in the area between the Tigris and Euphrates rivers, was one of the first places where civilization was recorded. Towns and communities were thriving here 6,000 years ago. The Arabian Peninsula *(see pp. 12-13)* is also part of the Middle East—a region that has about 75 percent of the world's oil reserves.

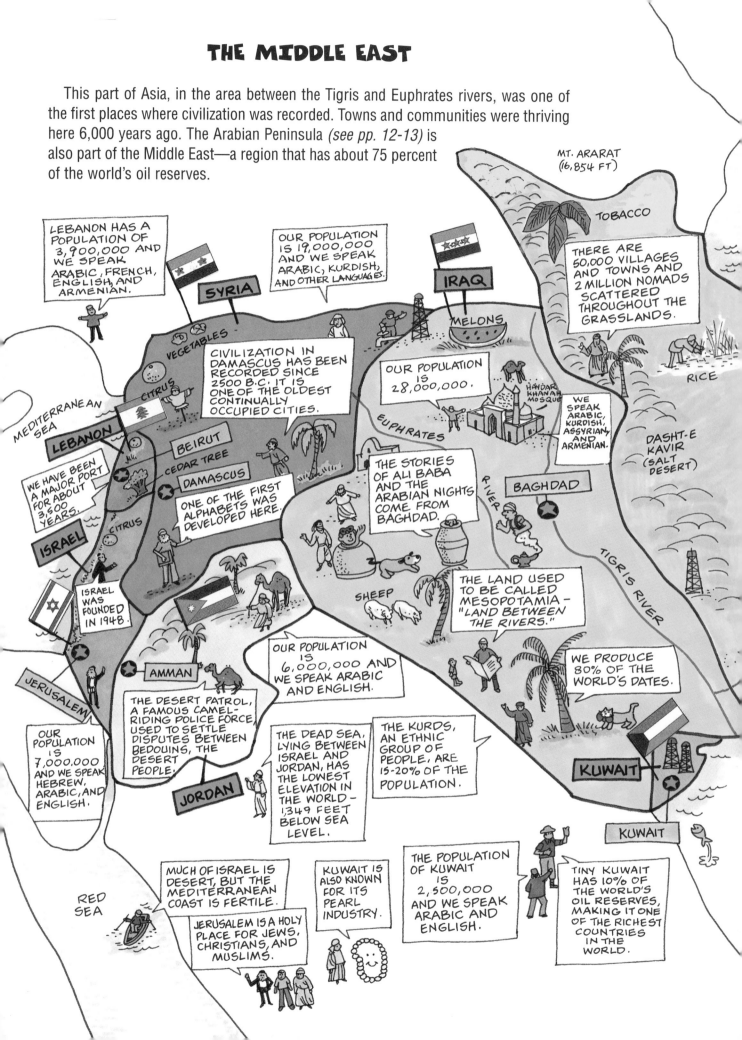

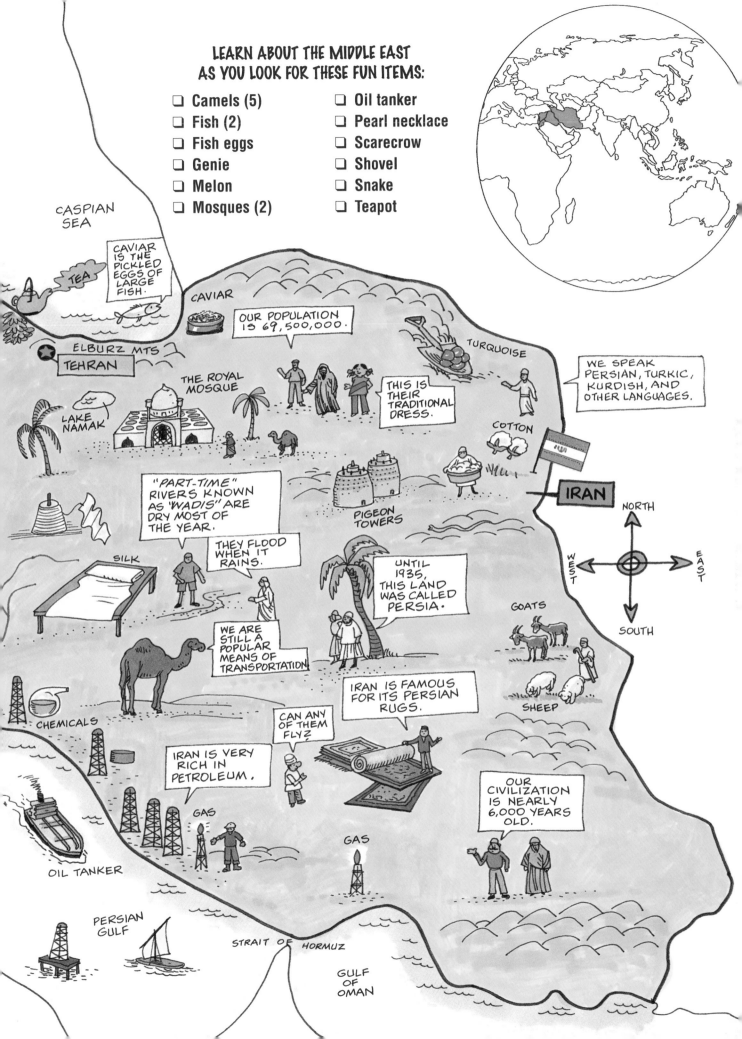

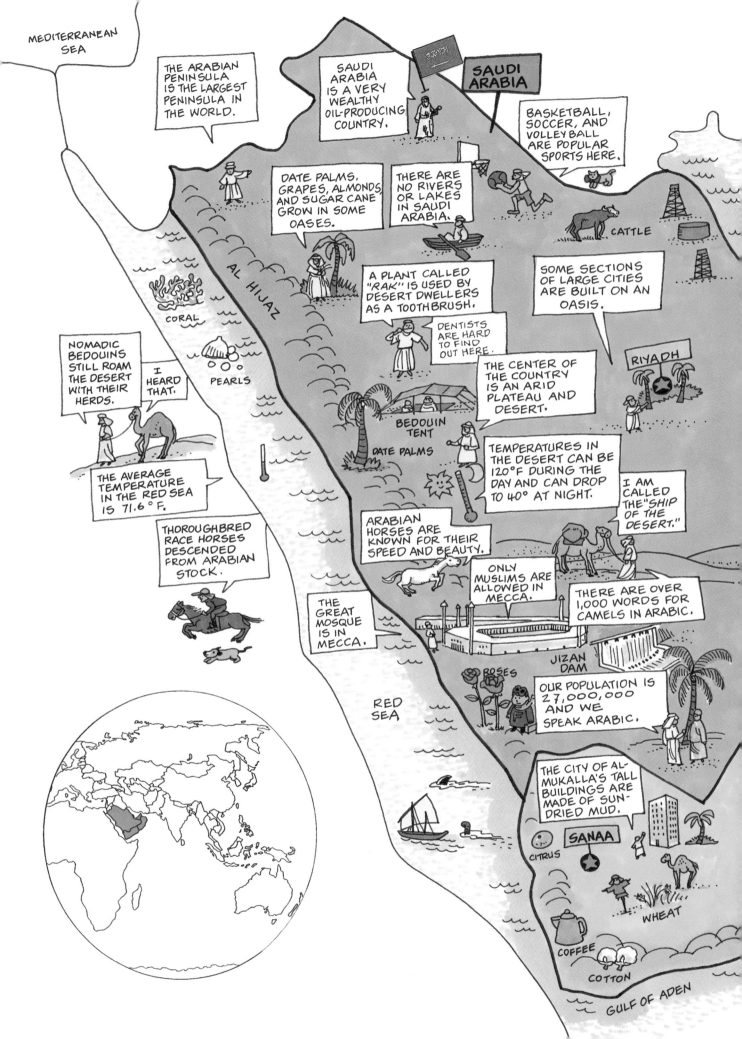

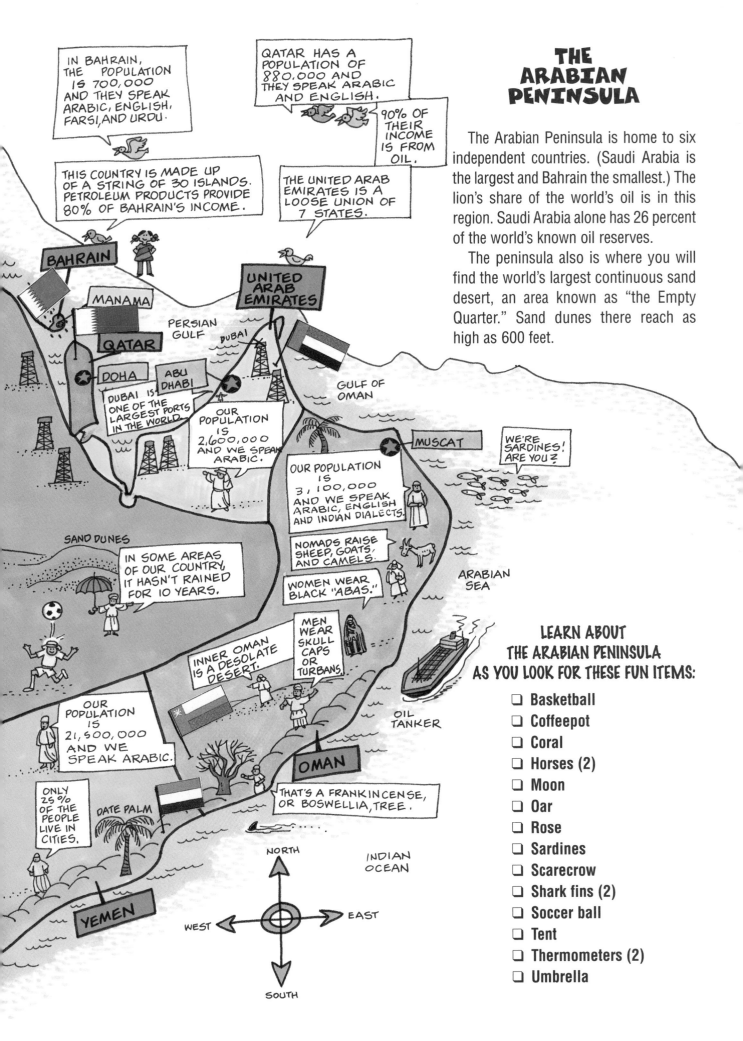

THE ARABIAN PENINSULA

The Arabian Peninsula is home to six independent countries. (Saudi Arabia is the largest and Bahrain the smallest.) The lion's share of the world's oil is in this region. Saudi Arabia alone has 26 percent of the world's known oil reserves.

The peninsula also is where you will find the world's largest continuous sand desert, an area known as "the Empty Quarter." Sand dunes there reach as high as 600 feet.

LEARN ABOUT THE ARABIAN PENINSULA AS YOU LOOK FOR THESE FUN ITEMS:

- ❑ Basketball
- ❑ Coffeepot
- ❑ Coral
- ❑ Horses (2)
- ❑ Moon
- ❑ Oar
- ❑ Rose
- ❑ Sardines
- ❑ Scarecrow
- ❑ Shark fins (2)
- ❑ Soccer ball
- ❑ Tent
- ❑ Thermometers (2)
- ❑ Umbrella

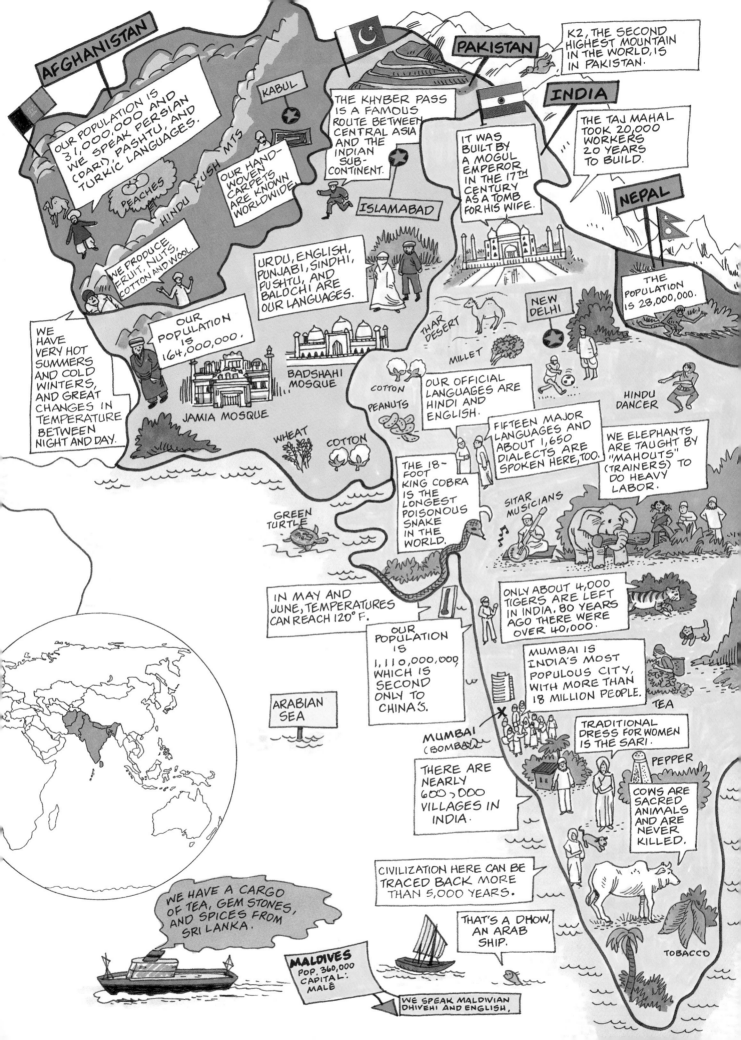

THE INDIAN SUBCONTINENT

South-central Asia—where a large area of land juts into the Indian Ocean—is referred to as the Indian subcontinent. About 70 percent of the people in this heavily populated region depend on the land for their livelihood.

India is one of only two countries in the world with more than one billion people. (China is the other.) The other countries in this region are Afghanistan, Pakistan, Nepal, Bhutan, Bangladesh, and Sri Lanka. About 400 miles southwest of Sri Lanka is a group of small islands that make up the country of Maldives.

LEARN ABOUT THE INDIAN SUBCONTINENT AS YOU LOOK FOR THESE FUN ITEMS:

- ❏ Bear
- ❏ Camels (2)
- ❏ Carpets (2)
- ❏ Cow
- ❏ Dancer
- ❏ Elephants (2)
- ❏ Fish (2)
- ❏ Monkeys (2)
- ❏ Musicians (2)
- ❏ Peanuts
- ❏ Pepper
- ❏ Snakes (2)
- ❏ Soccer ball
- ❏ Rhinoceros
- ❏ Turtle
- ❏ Umbrella

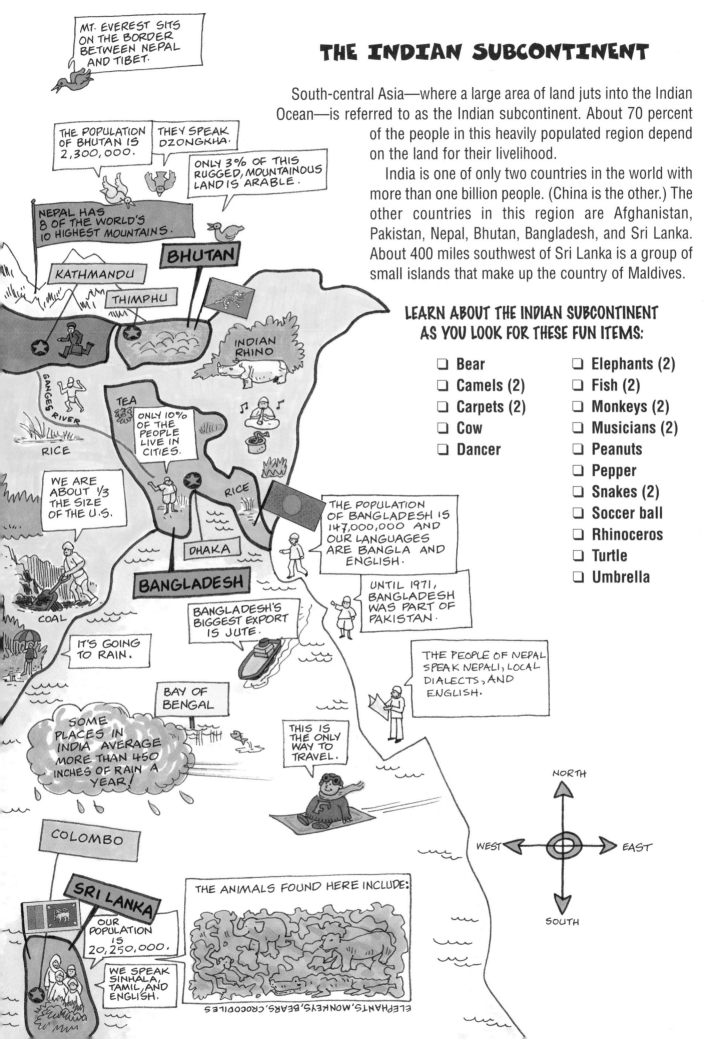

MT. EVEREST SITS ON THE BORDER BETWEEN NEPAL AND TIBET.

THE POPULATION OF BHUTAN IS 2,300,000.

THEY SPEAK DZONGKHA.

ONLY 3% OF THIS RUGGED, MOUNTAINOUS LAND IS ARABLE.

NEPAL HAS 8 OF THE WORLD'S 10 HIGHEST MOUNTAINS.

BHUTAN

KATHMANDU

THIMPHU

INDIAN RHINO

GANGES RIVER

RICE

TEA

ONLY 10% OF THE PEOPLE LIVE IN CITIES.

WE ARE ABOUT ⅓ THE SIZE OF THE U.S.

RICE

THE POPULATION OF BANGLADESH IS 147,000,000 AND OUR LANGUAGES ARE BANGLA AND ENGLISH.

DHAKA

BANGLADESH

COAL

UNTIL 1971, BANGLADESH WAS PART OF PAKISTAN.

BANGLADESH'S BIGGEST EXPORT IS JUTE.

IT'S GOING TO RAIN.

THE PEOPLE OF NEPAL SPEAK NEPALI, LOCAL DIALECTS, AND ENGLISH.

BAY OF BENGAL

SOME PLACES IN INDIA AVERAGE MORE THAN 450 INCHES OF RAIN A YEAR!

THIS IS THE ONLY WAY TO TRAVEL.

COLOMBO

SRI LANKA

OUR POPULATION IS 20,250,000.

WE SPEAK SINHALA, TAMIL, AND ENGLISH.

THE ANIMALS FOUND HERE INCLUDE:

ELEPHANTS, MONKEYS, BEARS, CROCODILES

NORTH

WEST EAST

SOUTH

CHINA AND NORTHEASTERN ASIA

China is the world's third-largest country in land area and first in population. (One out of every five people on Earth lives in China.) Much of China and the Korean peninsula is mountainous. The world's highest mountains, the Himalayas, are in Tibet, a region of China.

LEARN ABOUT CHINA AND NORTHEASTERN ASIA AS YOU LOOK FOR THESE FUN ITEMS:

❑ Bicycles (5)
❑ Camel
❑ Clay soldiers
❑ Ducks (3)
❑ Flying saucer
❑ Genghis Khan
❑ Horse
❑ Junk
❑ Mongol tent
❑ Pandas (2)
❑ Vulture
❑ Yaks (2)

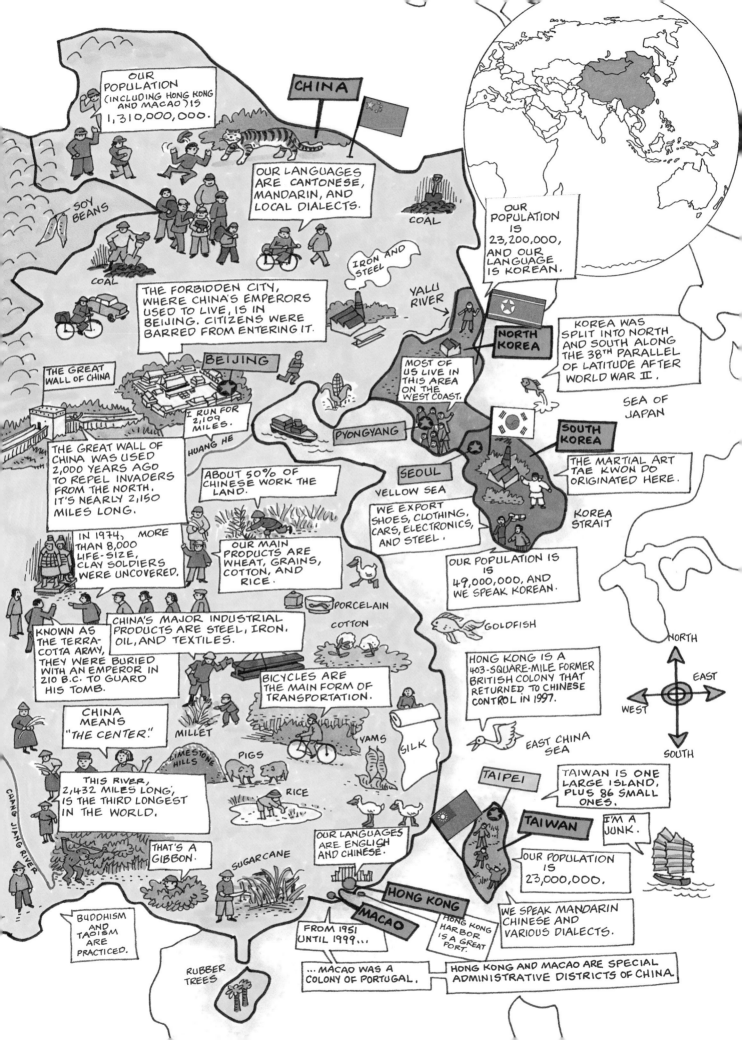

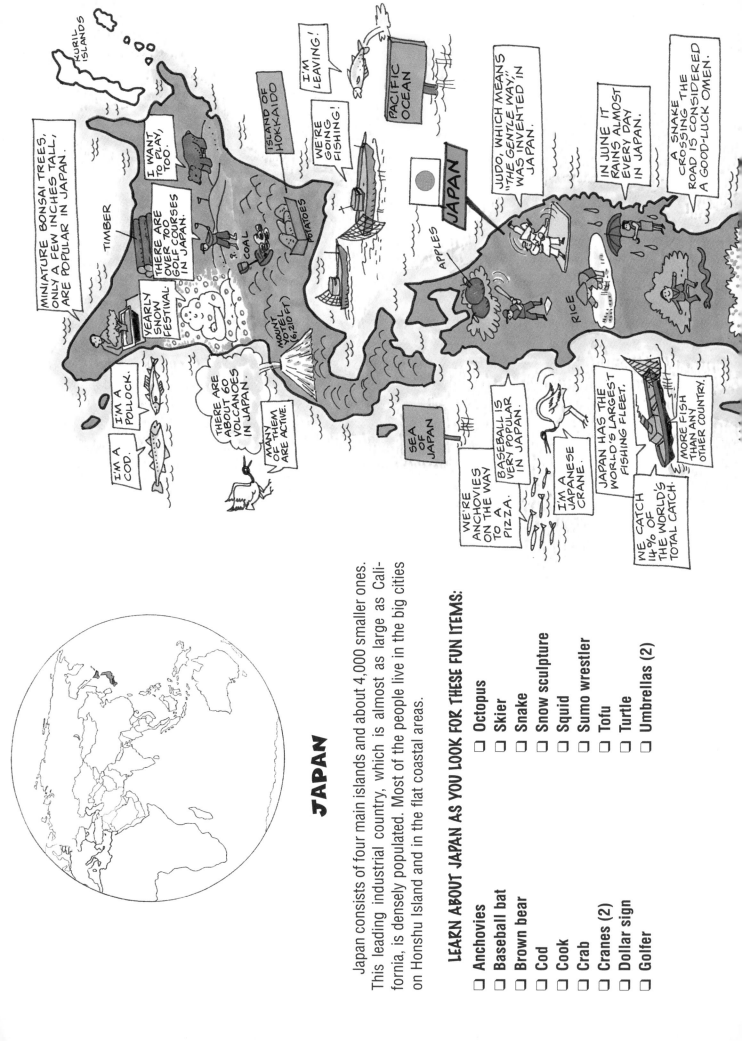

JAPAN

Japan consists of four main islands and about 4,000 smaller ones. This leading industrial country, which is almost as large as California, is densely populated. Most of the people live in the big cities on Honshu Island and in the flat coastal areas.

LEARN ABOUT JAPAN AS YOU LOOK FOR THESE FUN ITEMS:

- ☐ Anchovies
- ☐ Baseball bat
- ☐ Brown bear
- ☐ Cod
- ☐ Cook
- ☐ Crab
- ☐ Cranes (2)
- ☐ Dollar sign
- ☐ Golfer
- ☐ Octopus
- ☐ Skier
- ☐ Snake
- ☐ Snow sculpture
- ☐ Squid
- ☐ Sumo wrestler
- ☐ Tofu
- ☐ Turtle
- ☐ Umbrellas (2)

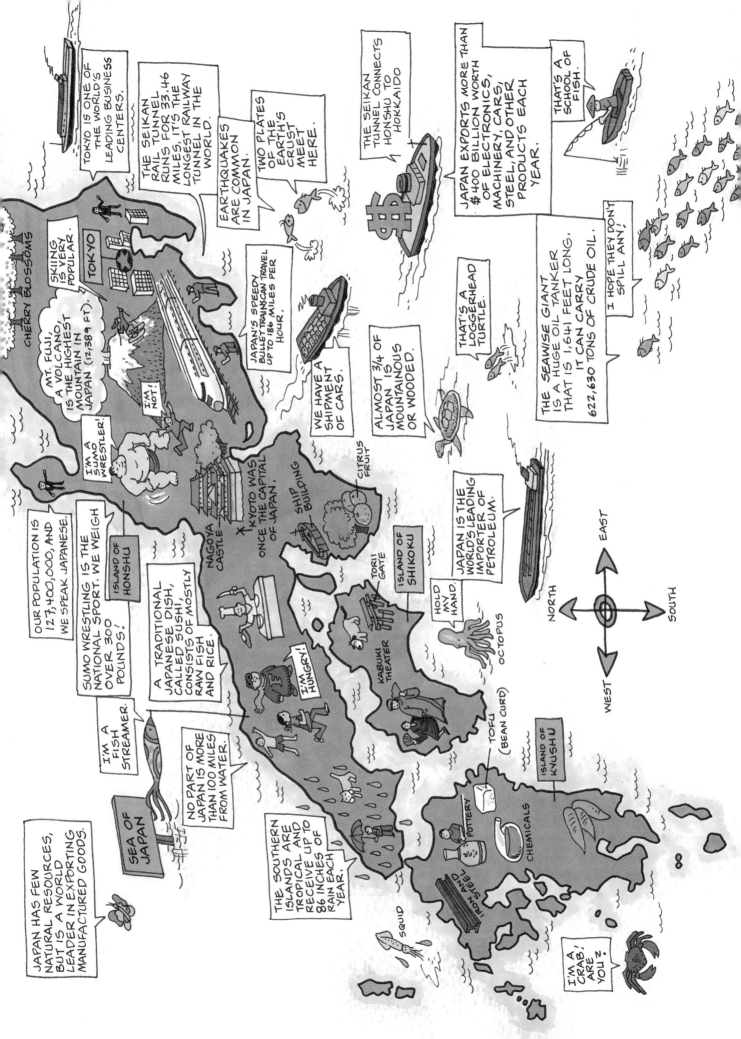

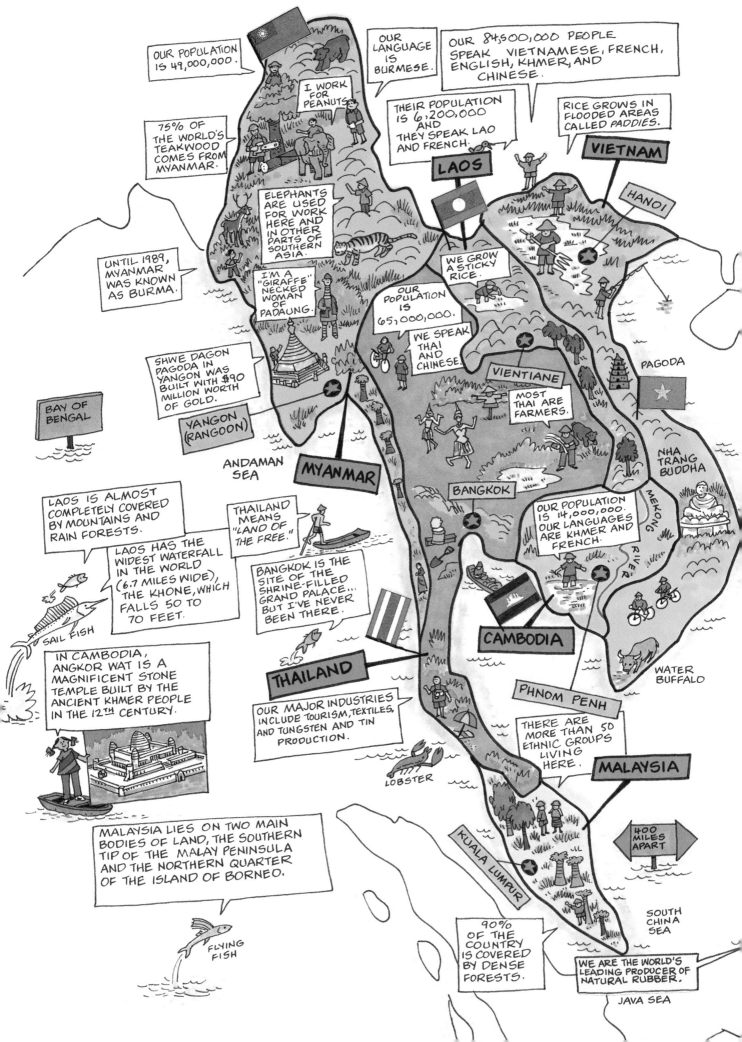

SOUTHEAST ASIA

This region is close to the equator, giving it a tropical climate with periods of heavy rainfall. Dense jungles or tropical rain forests cover much of the area, which has three main types of landscape: mountains, plains, or high, flat areas called plateaus. Most people here live near water—oceans, seas, or mighty rivers. Many Southeast Asians use the waterways for irrigating farmland, fishing, and transportation.

LEARN ABOUT SOUTHEAST ASIA
AS YOU LOOK FOR THESE FUN ITEMS:

- ❑ Brown bears (2)
- ❑ Cyclists (3)
- ❑ Dancers
- ❑ Deer
- ❑ Elephant
- ❑ Fisherman
- ❑ Flying fish
- ❑ "Giraffe" necked woman
- ❑ Lobster
- ❑ Pitchfork
- ❑ Scarecrow
- ❑ Tiger
- ❑ Umbrellas (2)

MORE THAN 60% OF THE VIETNAMESE FARM OR FISH.

SOUTH CHINA SEA

VIETNAM HAS A VERY TROPICAL CLIMATE.

DURING THE MONSOON SEASON, STRONG WINDS AND HEAVY RAINS ARE COMMON, ESPECIALLY IN THE SOUTHERN REGIONS.

THEY HAVE ONLY TWO SEASONS – A WET, HOT SUMMER AND A COOL WINTER.

THE HEART OF CAMBODIA IS THE RIVER BASIN WATERED BY THE MEKONG RIVER.

THE MEKONG RIVER CREATES FERTILE FARMING AREAS WHERE MAINLY RICE AND CORN ARE GROWN.

NORTH
WEST — EAST
SOUTH

MALAYSIA

BANDAR SERI BEGAWAN

WE MAKE A BEAUTIFUL HANDWOVEN CLOTH WITH GOLD AND SILVER THREADS.

THE POPULATION OF BRUNEI IS 400,000.
THEY SPEAK MALAY, CHINESE AND ENGLISH.

BRUNEI

BATIK IS A WAY OF PRINTING FABRIC HERE.

THE WORLD'S LARGEST CAVE CHAMBER IS IN SARAWAK, MALAYSIA. IT'S LARGE ENOUGH TO HOLD ABOUT 7,500 BUSES.

THE POPULATION OF MALAYSIA IS 25,000,000 AND THEY SPEAK BAHASA MALAYSIA AND OTHER LANGUAGES.

BORNEO

ARE WE THERE, YET?

z

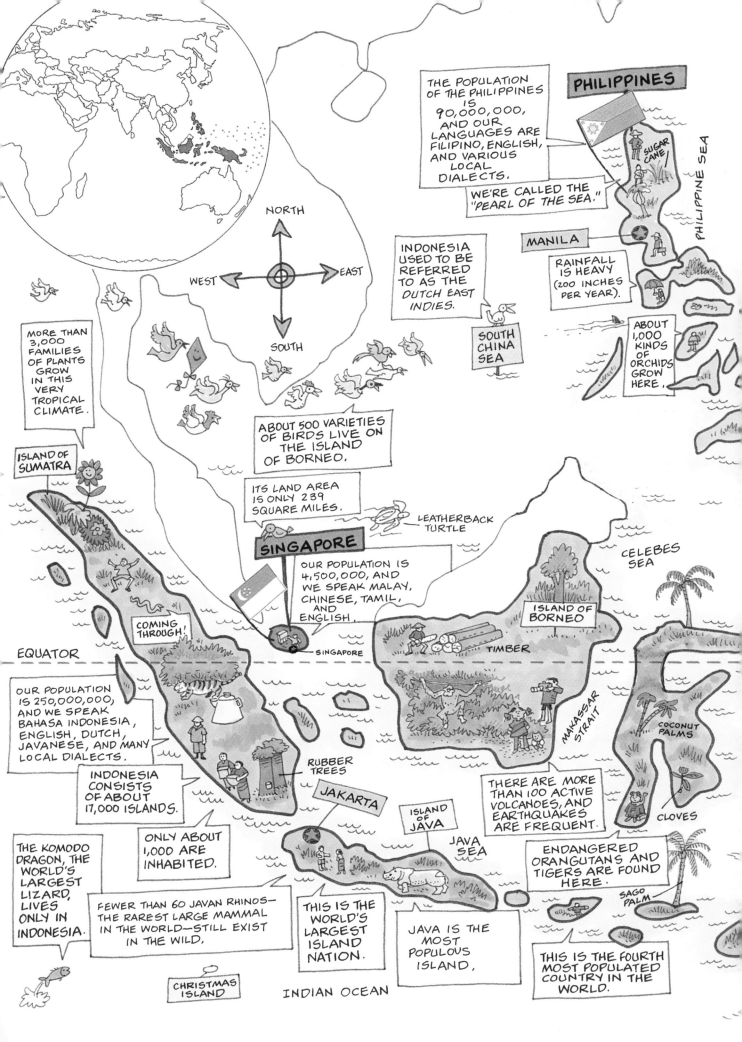

INDONESIA and PACIFIC ISLAND NATIONS

Indonesia, Singapore, the Philippines, and East Timor are part of Asia. Papua New Guinea and many small island nations scattered in this area of the Pacific Ocean are part of a region called Oceania. *(See p. 5 for a list of all the countries of Oceania.)* Most of this area has a hot, wet, tropical climate.

LEARN ABOUT INDONESIA AND PACIFIC ISLAND NATIONS AS YOU LOOK FOR THESE FUN ITEMS:

- ☐ Airplane
- ☐ Coffeepot
- ☐ Kite
- ☐ Orangutan
- ☐ Photographer
- ☐ Rhinoceros
- ☐ Shark fins (4)
- ☐ Tiger
- ☐ Tree kangaroo
- ☐ Turtle
- ☐ Tuna
- ☐ Volcanoes (2)

THE CLIMATE IS HOT AND HUMID.

OVER 80° IS THE AVERAGE TEMPERATURE.

THERE ARE OVER 7,000 ISLANDS IN THE PHILIPPINES, MOST OF THE PEOPLE LIVE ON THESE 11 ISLANDS.

BONIN ISLANDS (JAPAN)

OF ABOUT 25,000 ISLANDS IN THE PACIFIC OCEAN, ONLY A FEW THOUSAND ARE INHABITED.

NORTHERN MARIANA ISLANDS (U.S.)

WAKE ISLAND (U.S.)

NORTH PACIFIC OCEAN

MARSHALL ISLANDS

PALAU

SOME OF THE PACIFIC ISLANDS MAKE UP NINE INDEPENDENT COUNTRIES.

MANY OTHER ISLANDS ARE GOVERNED BY COUNTRIES SUCH AS THE U.S., GREAT BRITAIN, AND FRANCE.

VOLCANIC ERUPTIONS ARE COMMON. THESE ISLANDS ARE ACTUALLY THE TOPS OF MOUNTAINS THAT ARE STILL FORMING.

MICRONESIA

SOME OF THE ISLANDS ARE THE TIPS OF MOUNTAINS OR VOLCANOES, OTHERS ARE MADE UP OF CORAL.

I'M A PEARL OYSTER.

KIRIBATI

EQUATOR

PAPUA NEW GUINEA

OUR POPULATION IS 5,600,000, AND OUR LANGUAGES ARE ENGLISH, PIDGIN ENGLISH, MOTU, AND MANY OTHERS.

MOLUCCA SEA

INDONESIA

RAINFALL IS OVER 100 INCHES ANNUALLY.

HALF THE ISLAND BELONGS TO INDONESIA.

BISMARCK SEA

MT. WILHELM (14,790 FT)

TUVALU

TREE KANGAROO

BANDA SEA

INDONESIA'S MAIN EXPORTS ARE OIL, TIMBER, RUBBER AND COFFEE.

SOLOMON ISLANDS

DILI

EAST TIMOR

EAST TIMOR'S LANGUAGES ARE TETUM, PORTUGUESE, INDONESIAN, ENGLISH, AND OTHERS.

EAST TIMOR'S POPULATION IS 1,050,000.

EAST TIMOR—THE WORLD'S NEWEST COUNTRY—BECAME INDEPENDENT IN 2002.

PORT MORESBY

ARAFURA SEA

VANUATU

FIJI

CORAL SEA IS. (AUS.)

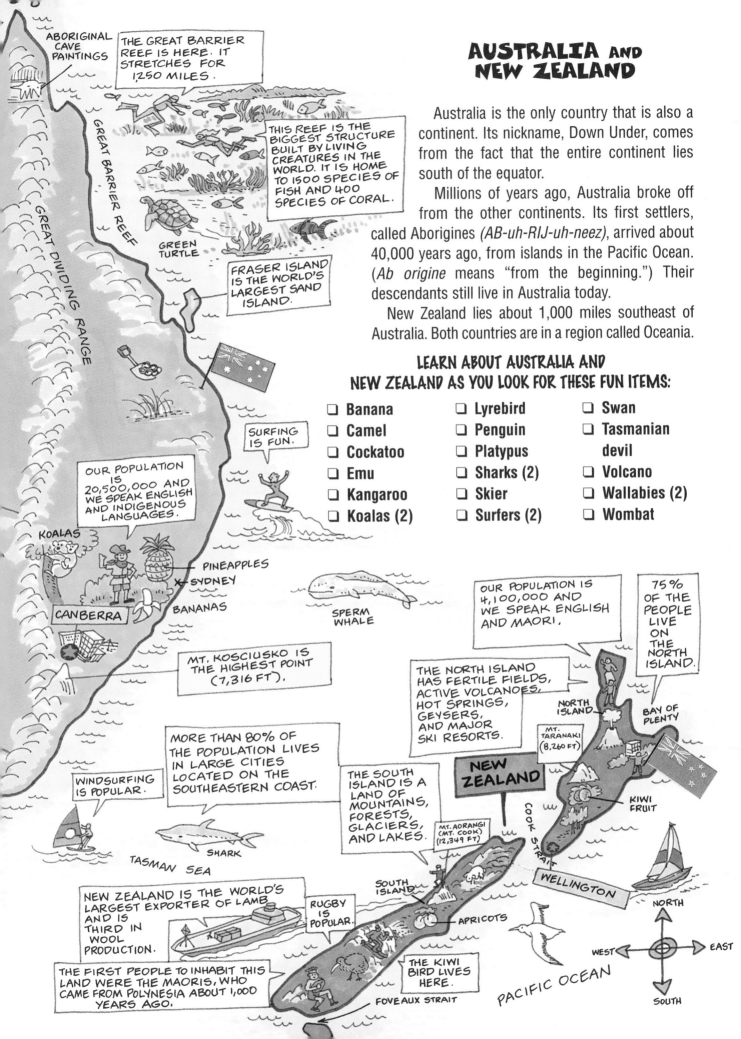

AUSTRALIA AND NEW ZEALAND

Australia is the only country that is also a continent. Its nickname, Down Under, comes from the fact that the entire continent lies south of the equator.

Millions of years ago, Australia broke off from the other continents. Its first settlers, called Aborigines *(AB-uh-RIJ-uh-neez)*, arrived about 40,000 years ago, from islands in the Pacific Ocean. (*Ab origine* means "from the beginning.") Their descendants still live in Australia today.

New Zealand lies about 1,000 miles southeast of Australia. Both countries are in a region called Oceania.

LEARN ABOUT AUSTRALIA AND NEW ZEALAND AS YOU LOOK FOR THESE FUN ITEMS:

❏ **Banana**
❏ **Camel**
❏ **Cockatoo**
❏ **Emu**
❏ **Kangaroo**
❏ **Koalas (2)**

❏ **Lyrebird**
❏ **Penguin**
❏ **Platypus**
❏ **Sharks (2)**
❏ **Skier**
❏ **Surfers (2)**

❏ **Swan**
❏ **Tasmanian devil**
❏ **Volcano**
❏ **Wallabies (2)**
❏ **Wombat**

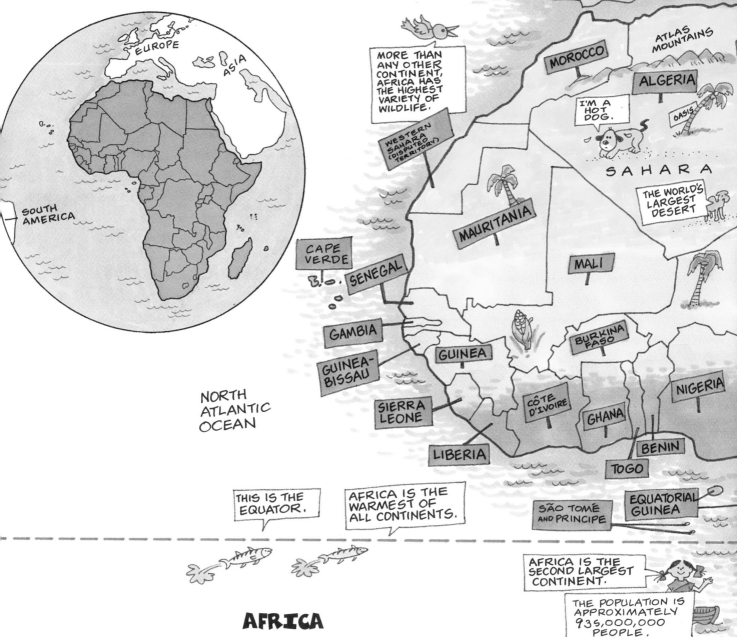

AFRICA

Once an unexplored and mysterious place to Europeans, Africa was known as the "Dark Continent." By the 19th century, European powers influenced or controlled much of Africa. However, starting in the late 1950s, country after country in Africa achieved its independence. The continent now is home to 53 independent nations. Africa's newest country, Eritrea, became independent in 1993, when it split from Ethiopia.

LEARN ABOUT AFRICA AS YOU LOOK FOR THESE FUN ITEMS:

- ❑ Atlas Mountains
- ❑ Butterfly
- ❑ Cape of Good Hope
- ❑ Elephant
- ❑ Gold bar
- ❑ Indian Ocean

- ❑ Mount Kilimanjaro
- ❑ Nile River
- ❑ Oil wells (2)
- ❑ Palm trees (4)
- ❑ Pyramid
- ❑ Rain cloud

- ❑ Rhinoceros
- ❑ Sea horse
- ❑ Sheep (2)
- ❑ Suez Canal
- ❑ Umbrella
- ❑ Zebra

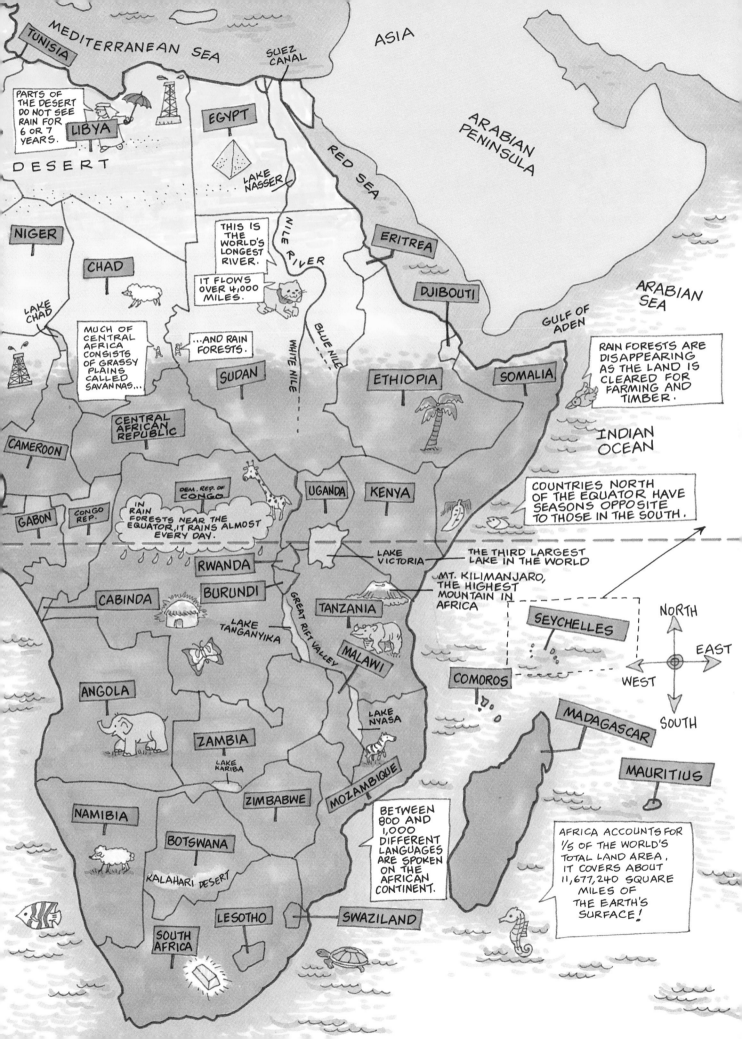

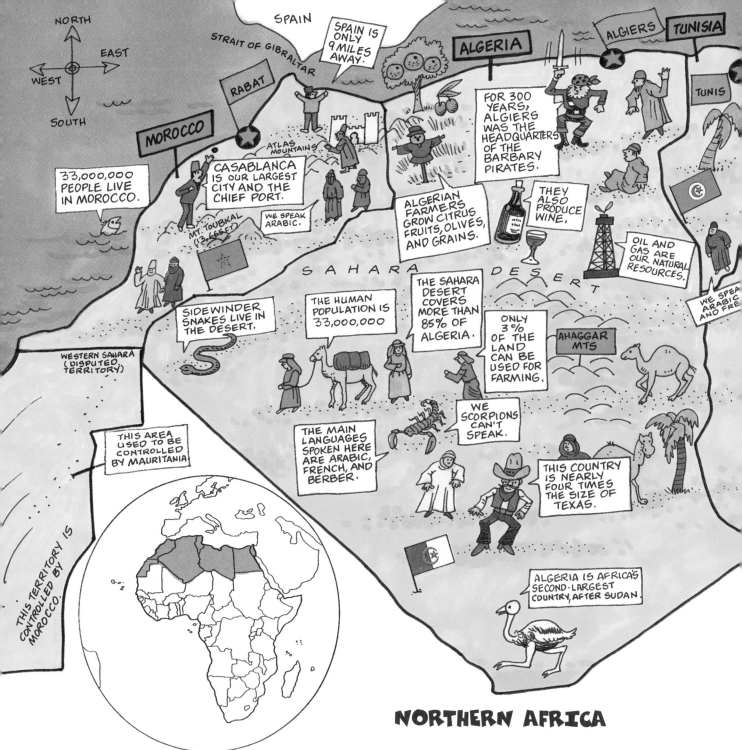

NORTHERN AFRICA

The peoples of ancient Greece, Rome, and Arabia influenced cultures in this part of Africa, and African culture—especially that of ancient Egypt—influenced them. In northern Africa today, Arabic is the dominant language and Islam is the major religion. Although Egypt is on the African continent, politically it often is considered part of the region known as the Middle East.

LEARN ABOUT NORTHERN AFRICA AS YOU LOOK FOR THESE FUN ITEMS:

- ❑ Barbary ape
- ❑ Beret
- ❑ Boats (3)
- ❑ Bunch of grapes
- ❑ Hyena
- ❑ Miner
- ❑ Mummy
- ❑ Orange tree
- ❑ Oil wells (4)
- ❑ Ostrich
- ❑ Palm trees (3)
- ❑ Pencil
- ❑ Pirate
- ❑ Pyramids (4)
- ❑ Scarecrow
- ❑ Scorpion
- ❑ Shovel
- ❑ Snake
- ❑ Thermometer

THE SAHEL

Just south of the Sahara Desert is a region called the Sahel, long inhabited by animal grazers and farmers. Much of the area is changing into desert as the Sahara expands southward at a rate of about three miles a year.

LEARN ABOUT THE SAHEL AS YOU LOOK FOR THESE FUN ITEMS:

- ❑ Anchor
- ❑ Basket
- ❑ Bird
- ❑ Camels (5)
- ❑ Cotton balls (3)
- ❑ Goat
- ❑ Elephant
- ❑ Fisherman
- ❑ Hippopotamus
- ❑ Lake Chad
- ❑ Niger River
- ❑ Peanuts (3)
- ❑ Periscope
- ❑ Soccer ball
- ❑ Sun
- ❑ Tent

THE HORN OF AFRICA

The region along Africa's northeastern coast is known as the Horn of Africa. On maps, its shape looks like the horn of a rhinoceros jutting into the Indian Ocean.

LEARN ABOUT THE HORN OF AFRICA AS YOU LOOK FOR THESE FUN ITEMS:

- ❏ Aardvark
- ❏ Acacia tree
- ❏ Banana
- ❏ Coffeepot
- ❏ Cotton
- ❏ Giraffes (2)
- ❏ Horseshoe

- ❏ Lion
- ❏ Marshmallow
- ❏ Nile crocodile
- ❏ Nubian Desert
- ❏ Oryx
- ❏ Ostrich
- ❏ Red Sea
- ❏ Umbrella
- ❏ White Nile
- ❏ Zebra

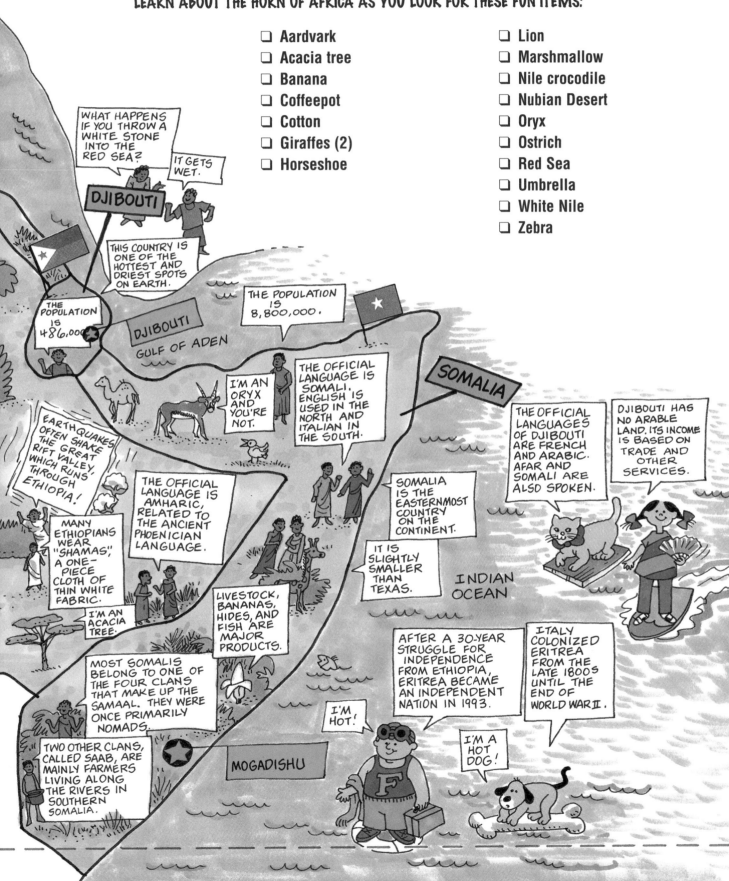

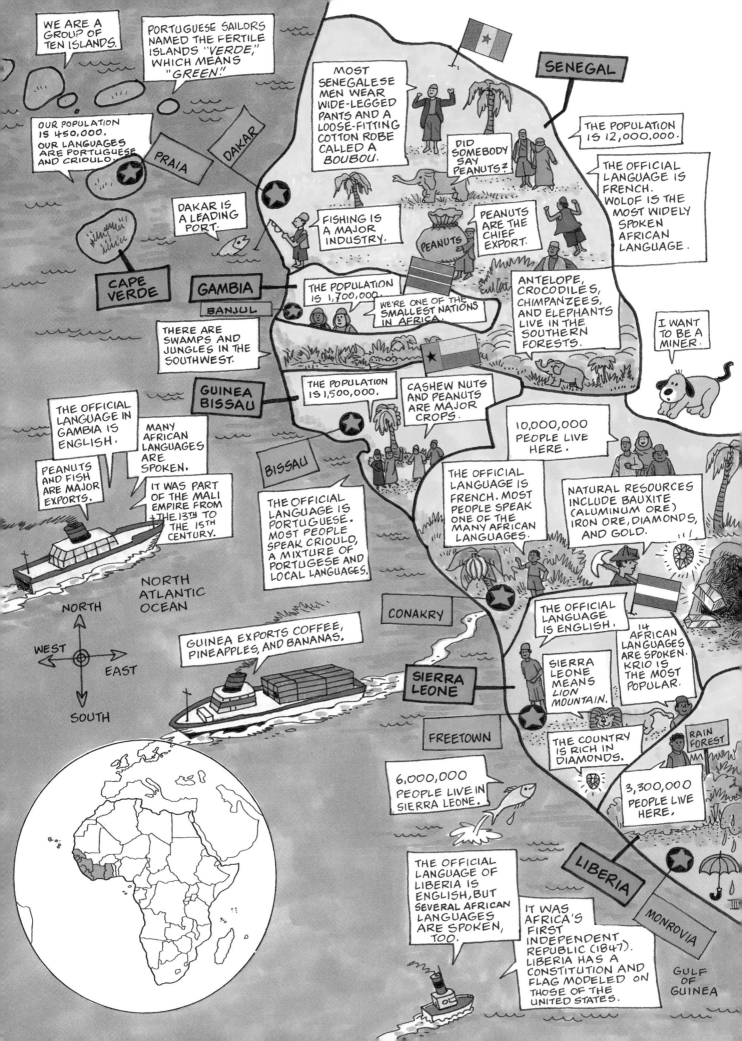

THE UPPER WEST COAST

Africa's upper west coast—the part that, seen on a map, bulges out into the Atlantic Ocean—has a landscape that varies from humid coastal plains and swamps to forested hills and plateaus. The soil is fertile, and farmers in this area grow such crops as cocoa, coffee, and peanuts.

During the era of the slave trade to the Americas, and for centuries before with other nations, coastal kingdoms of West Africa grew rich by trading slaves, gold, and ivory with Europeans.

LEARN ABOUT AFRICA'S UPPER WEST COAST AS YOU LOOK FOR THESE FUN ITEMS:

- ❑ Boats (4)
- ❑ Chocolate bar
- ❑ Coffeepot
- ❑ Crocodile
- ❑ Diamonds (4)
- ❑ Elephants
- ❑ Fisherman
- ❑ Game warden
- ❑ Gold bars (3)
- ❑ Lake Volta
- ❑ Lion
- ❑ Miner
- ❑ Pygmy hippopotamus
- ❑ Rain clouds (2)
- ❑ Umbrella

GUINEA

I'D LIKE A CHOCOLATE BAR.

CÔTE D'IVOIRE

I SEE A CUTE LION.

I LOVE PEANUTS.

GHANA

THE POPULATION IS 23,000,000.

THE OFFICIAL LANGUAGE IS ENGLISH, BUT THERE ARE MANY AFRICAN LANGUAGES SPOKEN HERE.

HISTORY IS RECITED BY STORYTELLERS CALLED GRIOTS.

THE POPULATION IS 18,000,000.

WE EXPORT COFFEE, COCOA, AND TROPICAL WOODS.

COCOA BEANS

THE OFFICIAL LANGUAGE IS FRENCH. AFRICAN LANGUAGES INCLUDE DIOULA, BAOULE, AND BETE.

BEFORE GAINING INDEPENDENCE FROM GREAT BRITAIN IN 1957, GHANA USED TO BE KNOWN AS THE GOLD COAST.

YAMOUSSOUKRO

THE COUNTRY WAS NAMED FOR THE IVORY TRADE, WHICH FLOURISHED FROM THE 13TH TO EARLY 20TH CENTURY.

RAIN FOREST

LAKE VOLTA

AN ENDANGERED SPECIES, THE PYGMY HIPPOPOTAMUS LIVES IN THE MARSHY SOUTHERN AREA OF GHANA.

WE EXPORT RUBBER, TIMBER, AND COCOA.

TODAY, IVORY TRADE IS ILLEGAL, AND THE NATION PROTECTS ITS ELEPHANTS IN GAME PRESERVES.

NATURAL RESOURCES INCLUDE GOLD, DIAMONDS, AND FISH.

ACCRA IS A MAJOR HUB FOR ROADS, RAILWAYS, AND SHIPPING.

LIBERIA WAS FOUNDED FOR THE SETTLEMENT OF FREED AMERICAN SLAVES.

NO HUNTING

IT'S SAFE HERE.

CHOCOLATE

ACCRA

COCOA BEANS ARE THE NUMBER-ONE EXPORT.

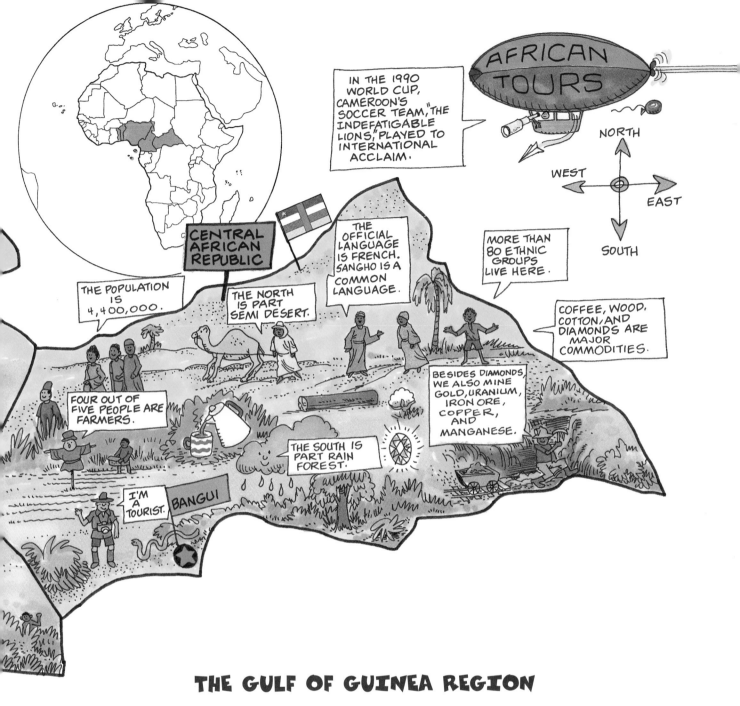

THE GULF OF GUINEA REGION

The Gulf of Guinea is a large section of the Atlantic that lies in the curve of Africa's bulging upper west coast. Many of the countries in this region share the "slave coast" history of the upper west coast countries (pp. 34-35). The gulf region has a richly varied landscape that includes old volcanic mountains, semidesert areas, swamps, tropical rain forests, and savannas. (*Savanna* is tropical or subtropical grassland.)

LEARN ABOUT AFRICA'S GULF OF GUINEA REGION AS YOU LOOK FOR THESE FUN ITEMS:

- ❑ Camera
- ❑ Cup
- ❑ Fishing poles (2)
- ❑ Giraffe
- ❑ Huts (2)
- ❑ Life preserver
- ❑ Oil wells (3)
- ❑ Paper airplane
- ❑ Red car
- ❑ Scarecrow
- ❑ Shark
- ❑ Snakes (2)
- ❑ Telescope
- ❑ Umbrellas (2)
- ❑ Volcano

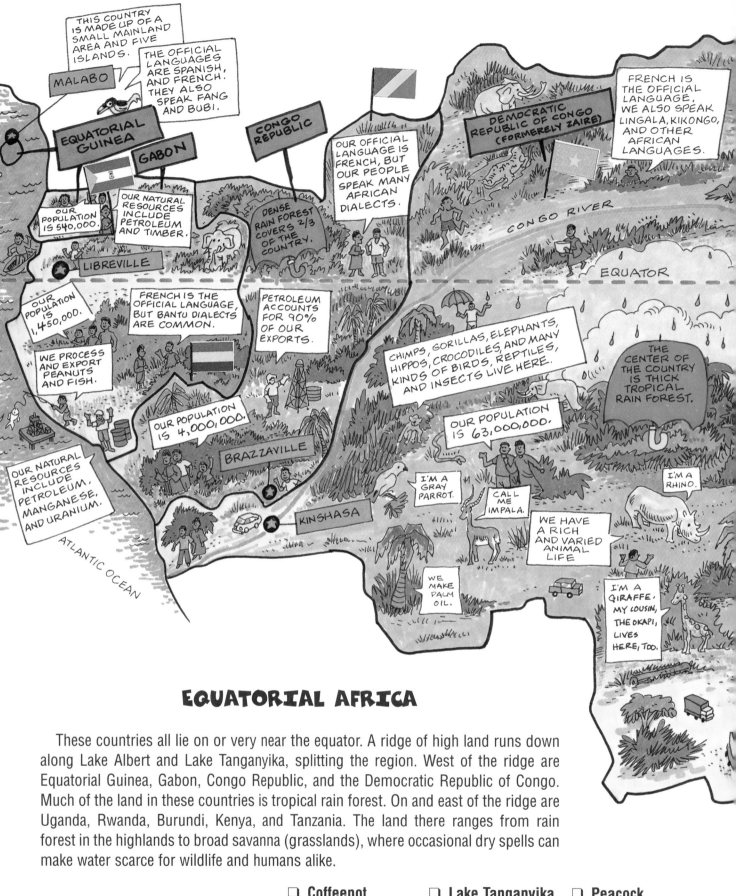

EQUATORIAL AFRICA

These countries all lie on or very near the equator. A ridge of high land runs down along Lake Albert and Lake Tanganyika, splitting the region. West of the ridge are Equatorial Guinea, Gabon, Congo Republic, and the Democratic Republic of Congo. Much of the land in these countries is tropical rain forest. On and east of the ridge are Uganda, Rwanda, Burundi, Kenya, and Tanzania. The land there ranges from rain forest in the highlands to broad savanna (grasslands), where occasional dry spells can make water scarce for wildlife and humans alike.

LEARN ABOUT EQUATORIAL AFRICA AS YOU LOOK FOR THESE FUN ITEMS:

- ❑ Coffeepot
- ❑ Congo River
- ❑ Crocodile
- ❑ Elephants (4)
- ❑ Gorilla
- ❑ Lake Tanganyika
- ❑ Lion
- ❑ Mount Kilimanjaro
- ❑ Parrot
- ❑ Peacock
- ❑ Snake
- ❑ Umbrellas (3)
- ❑ Zanzibar
- ❑ Zebra

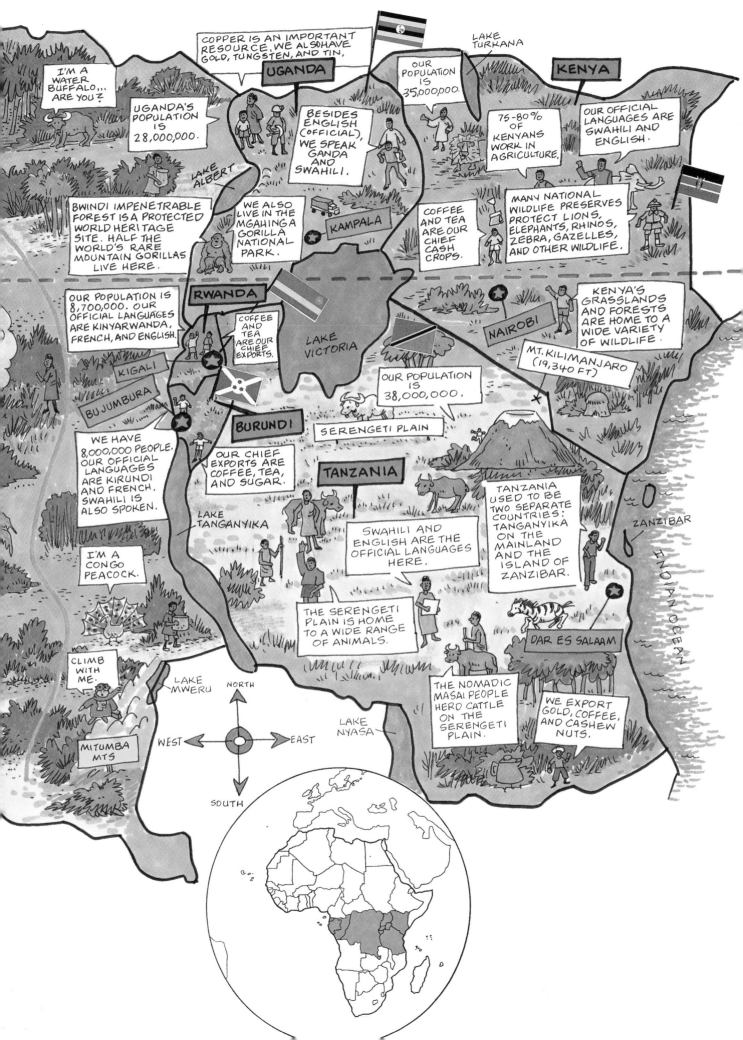

ANGOLA, ZAMBIA, MALAWI, AND MOZAMBIQUE

The region that lies south of the equatorial rain forests, between the South Atlantic Ocean and the Indian Ocean, has lots of open savanna and many farms. The area is home to antelope, elephants, giraffes, zebras, and many other animals.

LEARN ABOUT ANGOLA, ZAMBIA, MALAWI, AND MOZAMBIQUE AS YOU LOOK FOR THESE FUN ITEMS:

- ❑ Bananas (2)
- ❑ Cars (2)
- ❑ Coffee cups (2)
- ❑ Cow
- ❑ Eyeglasses
- ❑ Fish (3)
- ❑ Giraffe
- ❑ Hornbill
- ❑ Kariba Dam
- ❑ Leopard
- ❑ Rhinoceros
- ❑ Rice farmer
- ❑ Ring
- ❑ Scarecrow
- ❑ Shovel
- ❑ Snakes (2)
- ❑ Sun
- ❑ Victoria Falls

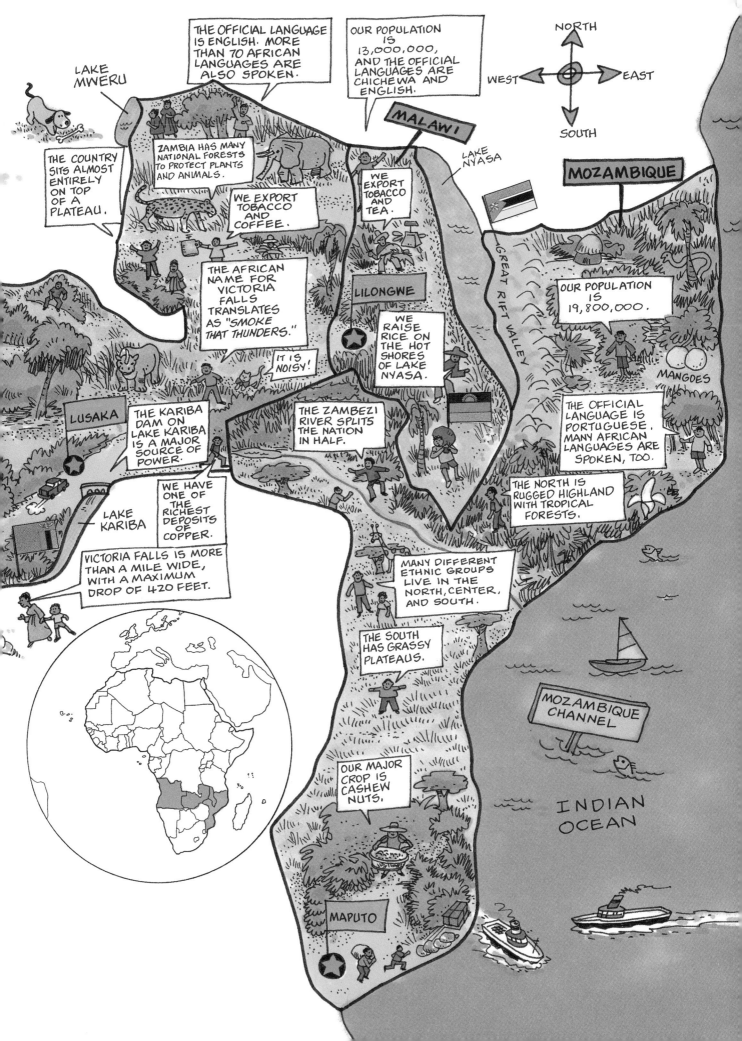

NAMIBIA, BOTSWANA, AND ZIMBABWE

Rich deposits of diamonds, gold, and minerals make this area one of the fastest-growing economic regions in Africa. Though rich in natural resources, such as diamonds and minerals, very little of the land in Namibia and Botswana is habitable. Namibia has only six people per square mile and Botswana has only seven. With its more-arable land and better-developed industries, Zimbabwe has 82 people per square mile.

LEARN ABOUT NAMIBIA, BOTSWANA, AND ZIMBABWE AS YOU LOOK FOR THESE FUN ITEMS:

- ❏ Baby
- ❏ Billboard
- ❏ Book
- ❏ Elephants (6)
- ❏ Fishing pole
- ❏ Lions (2)
- ❏ Lost snowman
- ❏ Namib Desert
- ❏ Oryx
- ❏ Picks (2)
- ❏ Rake
- ❏ Scorpion
- ❏ Shipwreck
- ❏ Snakes (5)
- ❏ Sneaker
- ❏ Snowman
- ❏ Truck
- ❏ Zebras (2)

SOUTH AFRICA, LESOTHO, AND SWAZILAND

The world's greatest diamond and gold mines are in South Africa, making it the richest country in Africa. The mines employ tens of thousands of men from neighboring countries.

Lesotho and Swaziland are two small, landlocked countries. One is completely surrounded by South Africa; the other is mostly so. Both are completely dependent on South Africa and Mozambique for trade routes to the ocean and other countries.

LEARN ABOUT SOUTH AFRICA, LESOTHO, AND SWAZILAND AS YOU LOOK FOR THESE FUN ITEMS:

- ❏ Cars (4)
- ❏ Citrus fruit
- ❏ Crown
- ❏ Drummer
- ❏ Giraffes (3)
- ❏ Grapes
- ❏ Guitar
- ❏ Lion
- ❏ Orange River
- ❏ Ostrich
- ❏ Pineapple
- ❏ Sailor
- ❏ Scarecrow
- ❏ Sheep (2)
- ❏ Shovel
- ❏ Table Mountain
- ❏ Tent
- ❏ Tractor
- ❏ Zebra
- ❏ Zulu warrior

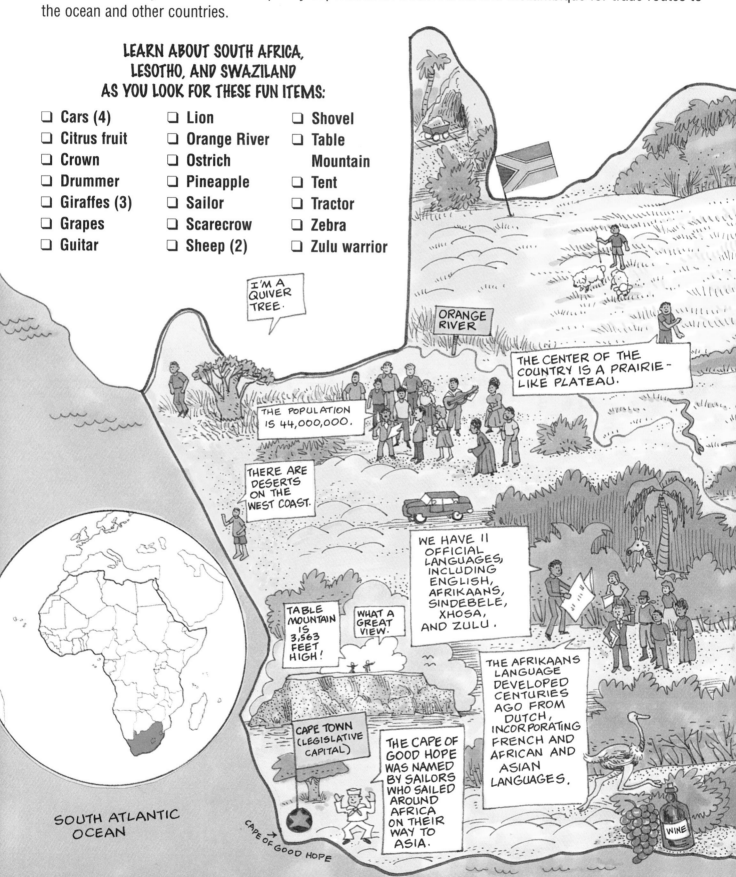

I'M A QUIVER TREE.

ORANGE RIVER

THE CENTER OF THE COUNTRY IS A PRAIRIE-LIKE PLATEAU.

THE POPULATION IS 44,000,000.

THERE ARE DESERTS ON THE WEST COAST.

WE HAVE 11 OFFICIAL LANGUAGES, INCLUDING ENGLISH, AFRIKAANS, SINDEBELE, XHOSA, AND ZULU.

TABLE MOUNTAIN IS 3,563 FEET HIGH!

WHAT A GREAT VIEW.

THE AFRIKAANS LANGUAGE DEVELOPED CENTURIES AGO FROM DUTCH, INCORPORATING FRENCH AND AFRICAN AND ASIAN LANGUAGES.

CAPE TOWN (LEGISLATIVE CAPITAL)

THE CAPE OF GOOD HOPE WAS NAMED BY SAILORS WHO SAILED AROUND AFRICA ON THEIR WAY TO ASIA.

SOUTH ATLANTIC OCEAN

CAPE OF GOOD HOPE

WINE

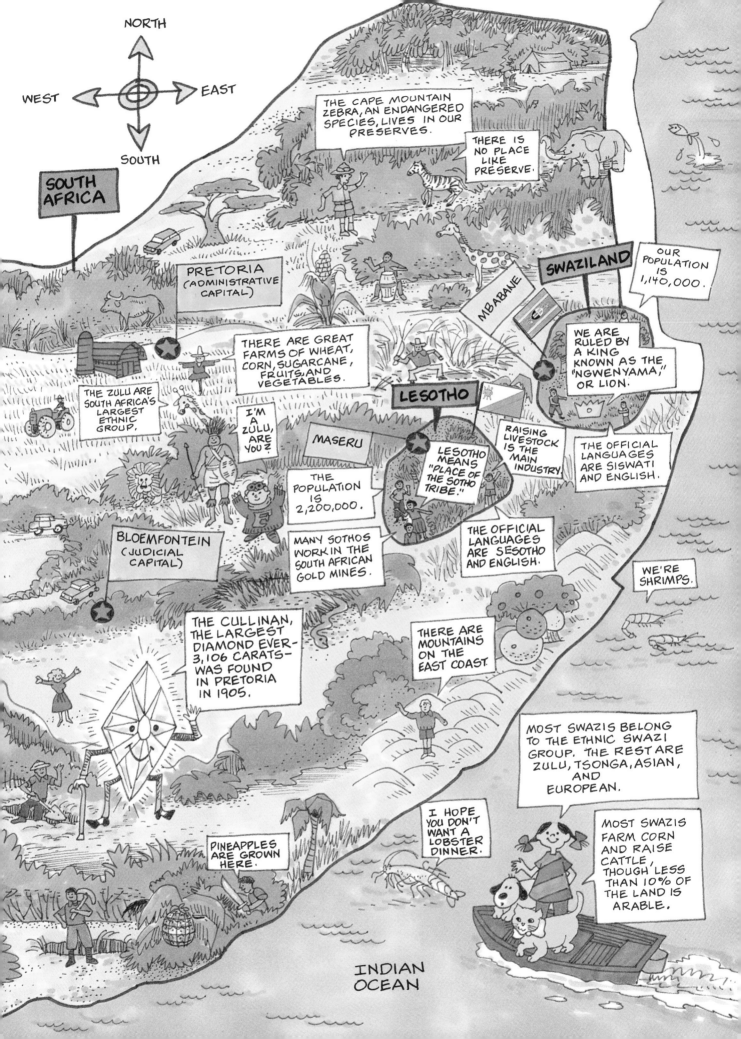

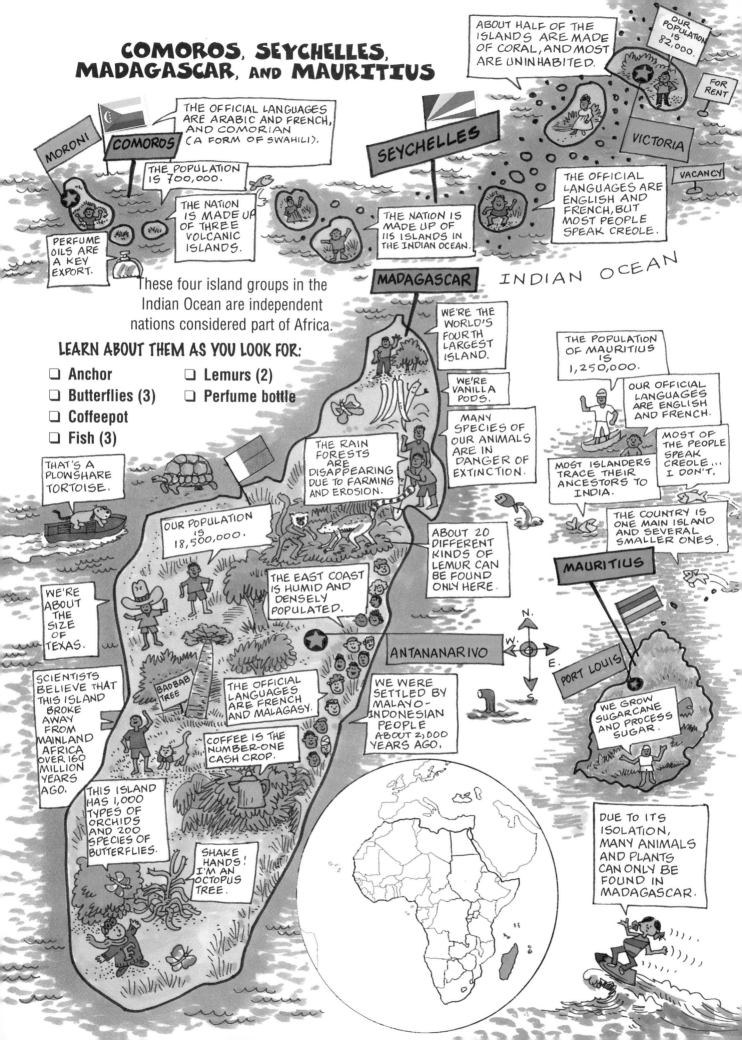

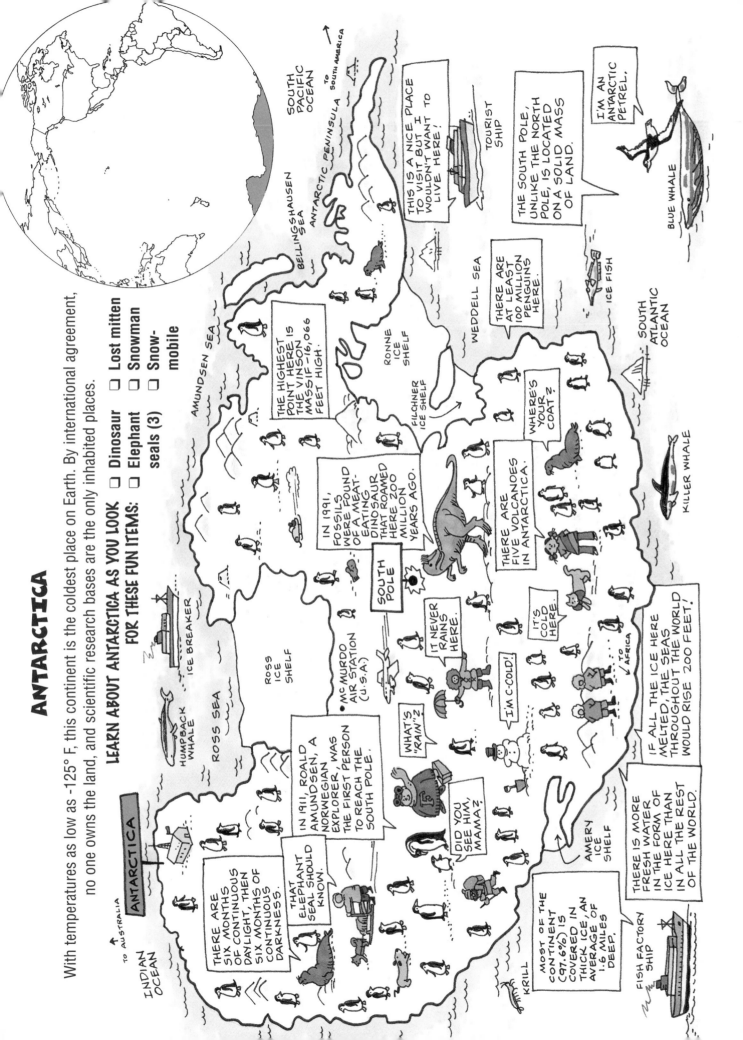

THE POPULATION OF SOUTH AMERICA IS ABOUT 380,000,000.

HOW DID THAT FISH KNOW THAT?

I'VE HEARD OF THAT!

SOUTH AMERICA COVERS 6,898,576 SQUARE MILES.

A GAUCHO IS A CATTLEHERDER.

THE STRONG WIND AND CURRENTS AROUND CAPE HORN HAVE MADE IT A GRAVEYARD FOR SHIPS.

BRAZIL

PARAGUAY

URUGUAY

AMAZON RIVER

THE ANDES MT. RANGE IS THE LONGEST RANGE IN THE WORLD.

THE MAIN LANGUAGE IN CENTRAL AND SOUTH AMERICA IS SPANISH—EXCEPT IN BRAZIL, WHERE PORTUGUESE IS SPOKEN.

BOLIVIA

ARGENTINA

ANDES MTS

ANDES MTS

LAKE TITICACA

CAPE HORN

PERU

ATACAMA DESERT

CHILE

ANTARCTIC CIRCLE

MOST OF SOUTH AMERICA IS BELOW THE EQUATOR, WHICH MEANS THAT SUMMER STARTS IN DECEMBER AND WINTER STARTS IN JUNE.

ECUADOR

NORTH AMERICA AND SOUTH AMERICA

North America is the third largest of the seven continents. It stretches from Greenland and Canada in the Arctic north to Panama, which is near the equator. Islands in the Caribbean Sea are are also part of North America.

South America is the fourth largest continent. From equatorial Colombia, it extends farther south than any continent except Antarctica.

LEARN ABOUT NORTH AND SOUTH AMERICA AS YOU LOOK FOR THESE FUN ITEMS:

☐ Banana
☐ Cactuses (2)
☐ Coffeepot
☐ Igloo
☐ Monkey

☐ Moose
☐ Parrot
☐ Penguin
☐ Periscope
☐ Sailboats (2)

☐ Shipwreck
☐ Snowman
☐ Soccer player
☐ Surfer
☐ Swordfish

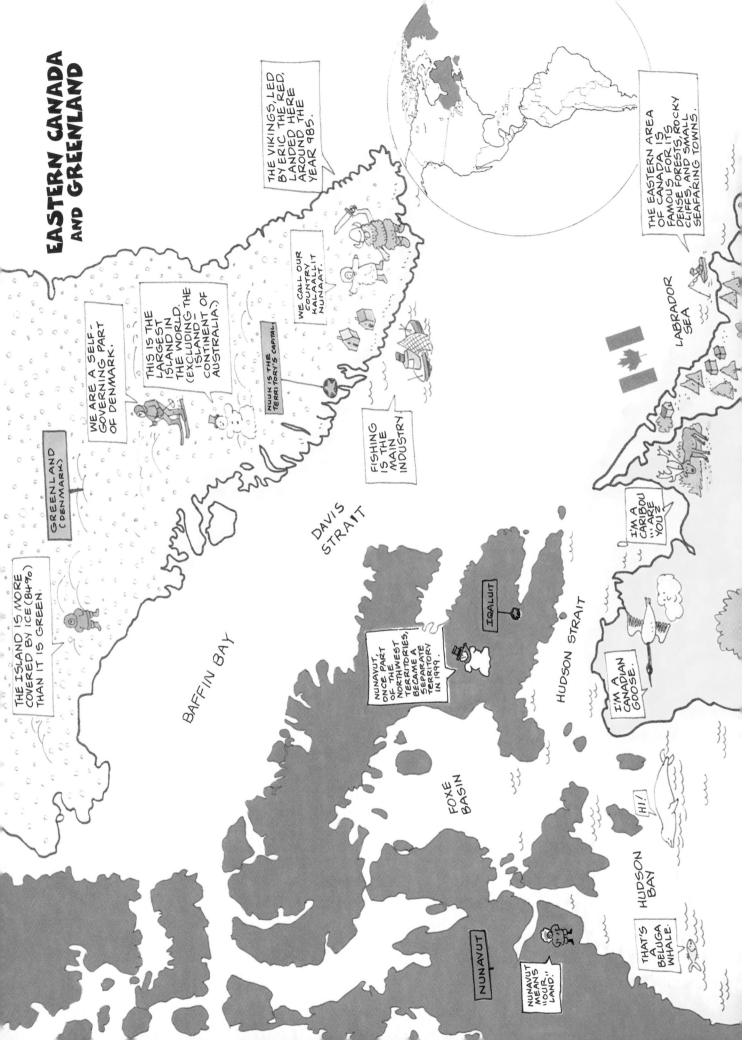

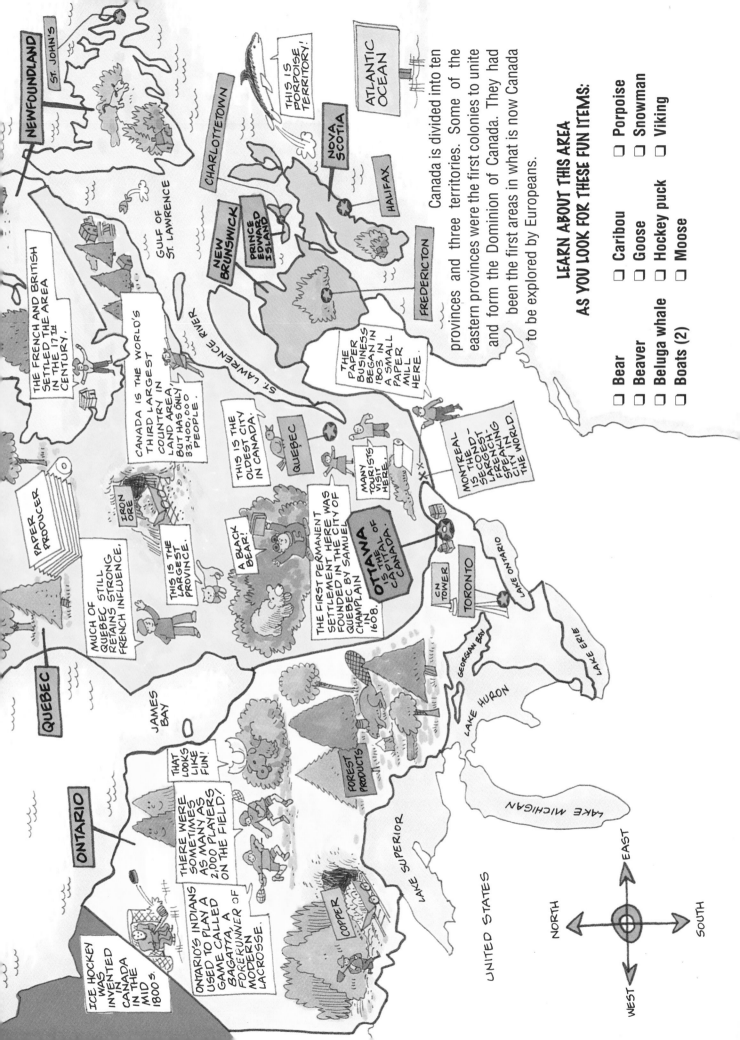

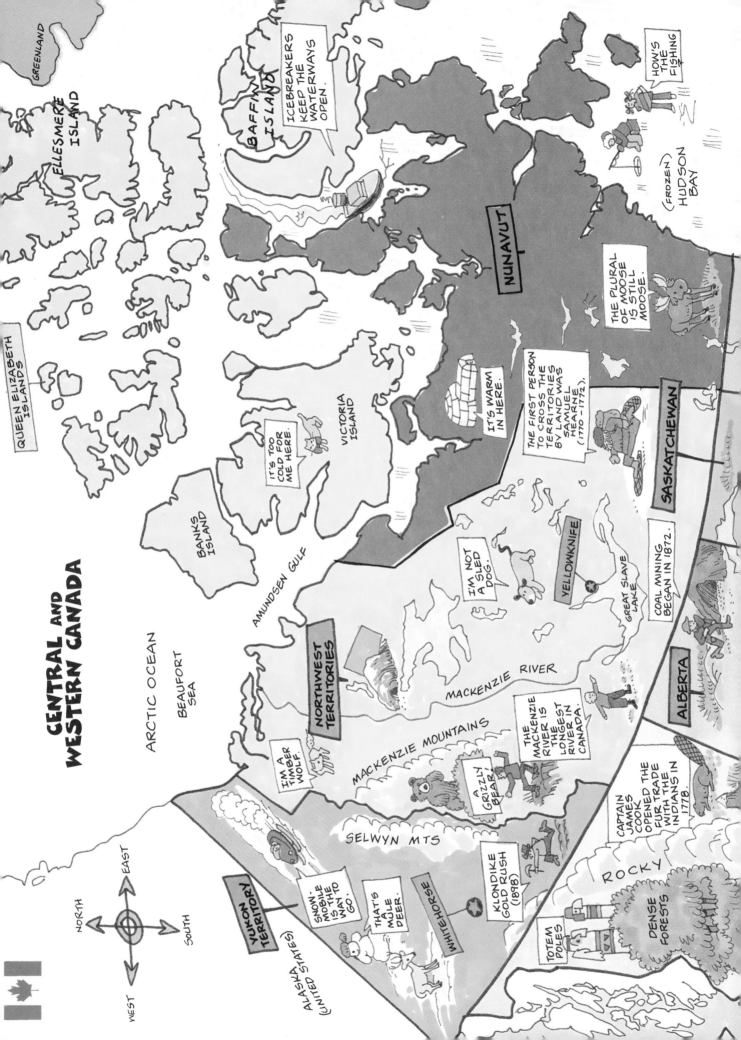

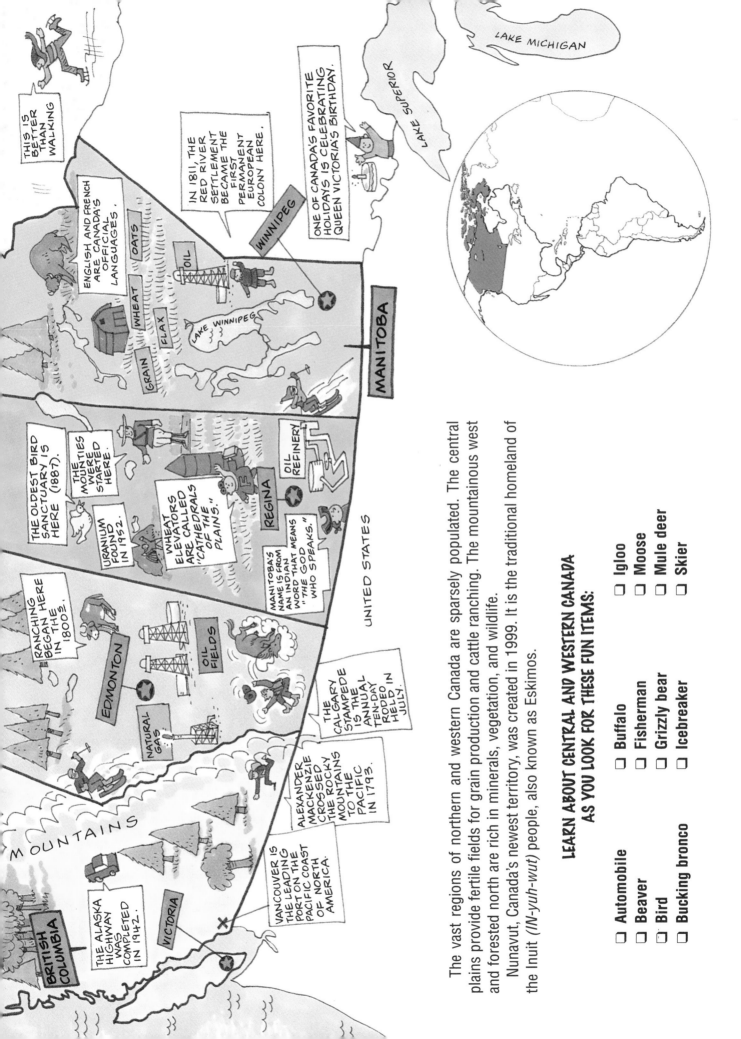

The vast regions of northern and western Canada are sparsely populated. The central plains provide fertile fields for grain production and cattle ranching. The mountainous west and forested north are rich in minerals, vegetation, and wildlife.

Nunavut, Canada's newest territory, was created in 1999. It is the traditional homeland of the Inuit (*IN-yuh-wut*) people, also known as Eskimos.

LEARN ABOUT CENTRAL AND WESTERN CANADA AS YOU LOOK FOR THESE FUN ITEMS:

☐ Automobile
☐ Beaver
☐ Bird
☐ Bucking bronco

☐ Buffalo
☐ Fisherman
☐ Grizzly bear
☐ Icebreaker

☐ Igloo
☐ Moose
☐ Mule deer
☐ Skier

THE UNITED STATES OF AMERICA

The United States of America is the world's third-largest country in population (after China and India) and the fourth-largest in land area (after Russia, China, and Canada). Its huge economic, political, and military influence make it the world's leading superpower.

In the 18th century, Britain ruled 13 American colonies. The U.S. became an independent nation in 1776, when it rebelled against British rule. Those colonies became the original 13 states. Today, the U.S. is a nation of 50 states. Washington, D.C., is the national capital and federal district. Outlying territories and other areas include Puerto Rico, the U.S. Virgin Islands, and Guam.

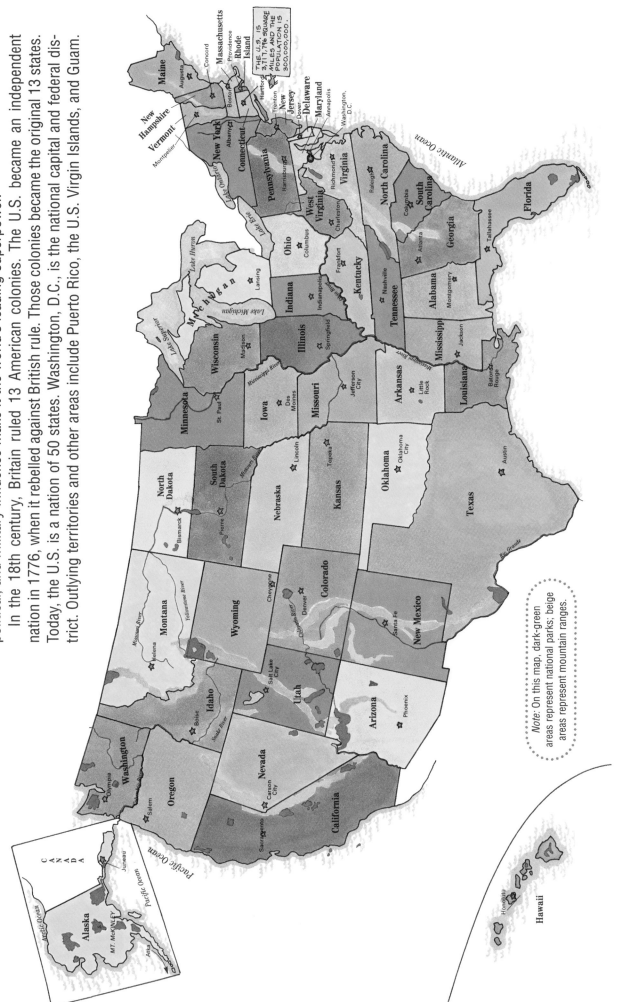

THE U.S. IS 3,717,796 SQUARE MILES AND THE POPULATION IS 300,000,000.

Note: On this map, dark-green areas represent national parks; beige areas represent mountain ranges.

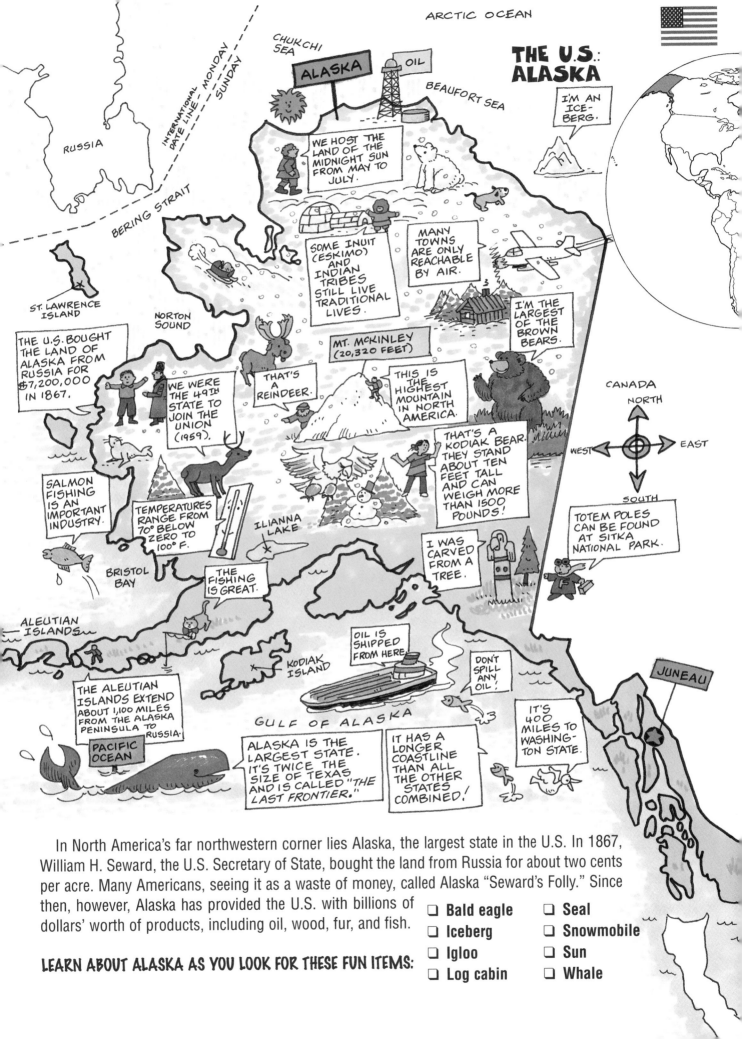

In North America's far northwestern corner lies Alaska, the largest state in the U.S. In 1867, William H. Seward, the U.S. Secretary of State, bought the land from Russia for about two cents per acre. Many Americans, seeing it as a waste of money, called Alaska "Seward's Folly." Since then, however, Alaska has provided the U.S. with billions of dollars' worth of products, including oil, wood, fur, and fish.

LEARN ABOUT ALASKA AS YOU LOOK FOR THESE FUN ITEMS:

- ❏ Bald eagle
- ❏ Iceberg
- ❏ Igloo
- ❏ Log cabin
- ❏ Seal
- ❏ Snowmobile
- ❏ Sun
- ❏ Whale

THE U.S.: THE WESTERN STATES

The western part of the country is characterized by deserts, mountains, river canyons, and great forests. Separated from the rest of the continental U.S. by the Rocky Mountains, parts of this area—especially along the coast—were rapidly settled and developed after railroads were built in the mid-19th century, linking west to east.

The Hawaiian Islands became a U.S. territory in 1900 and the 50th state in 1959.

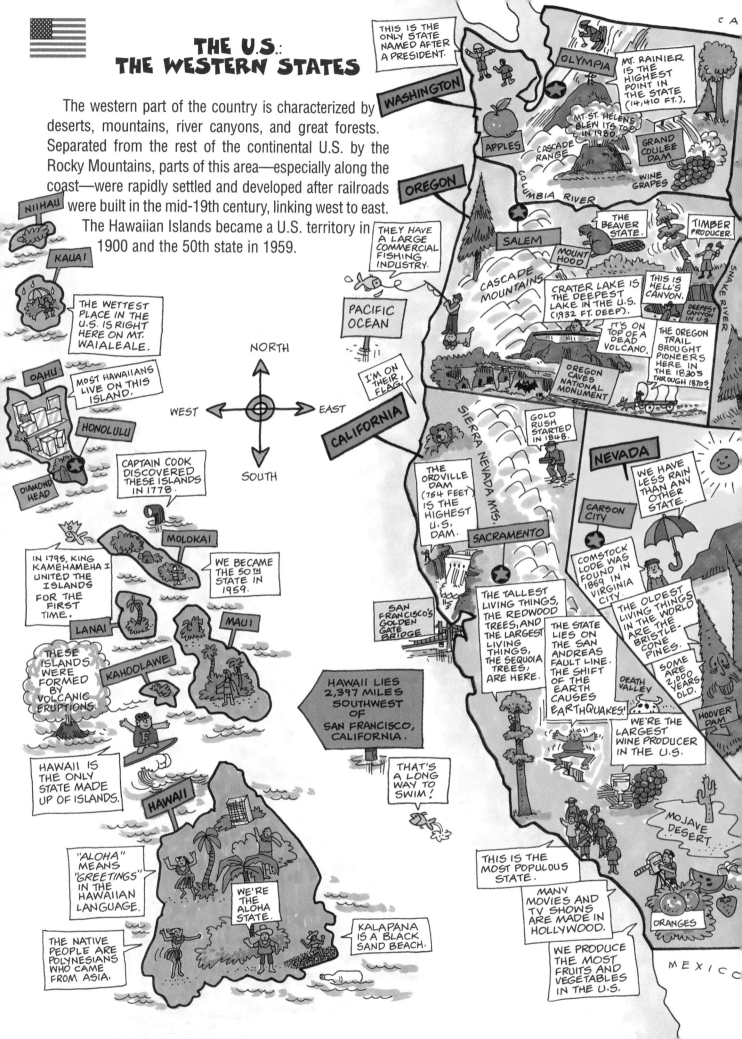

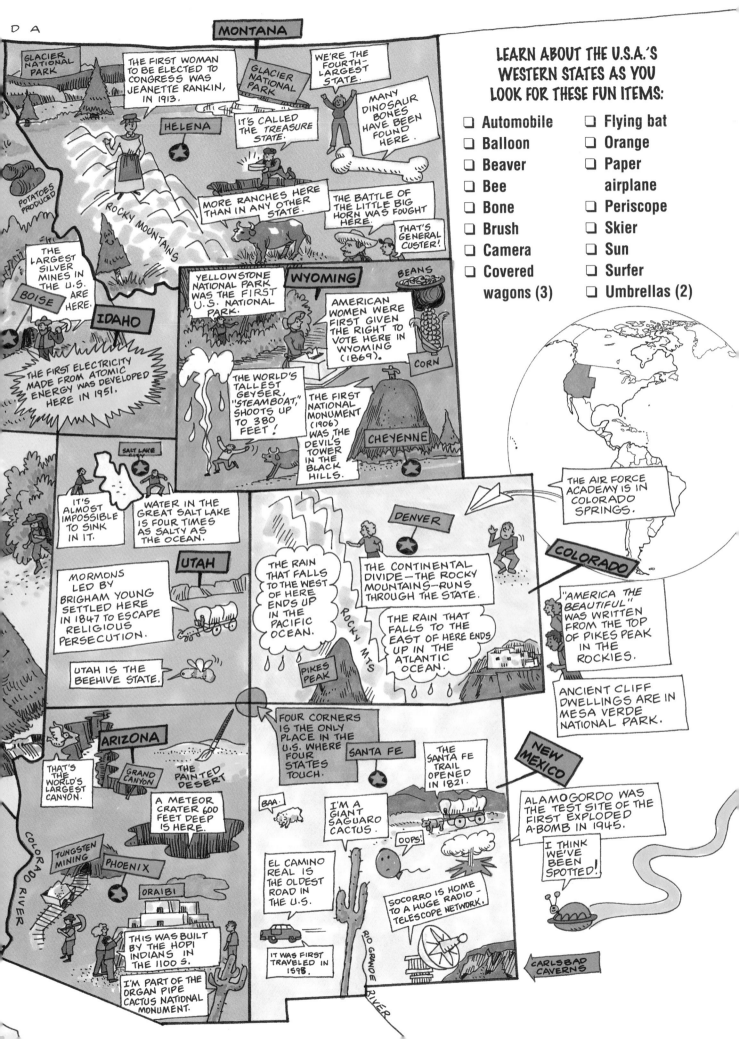

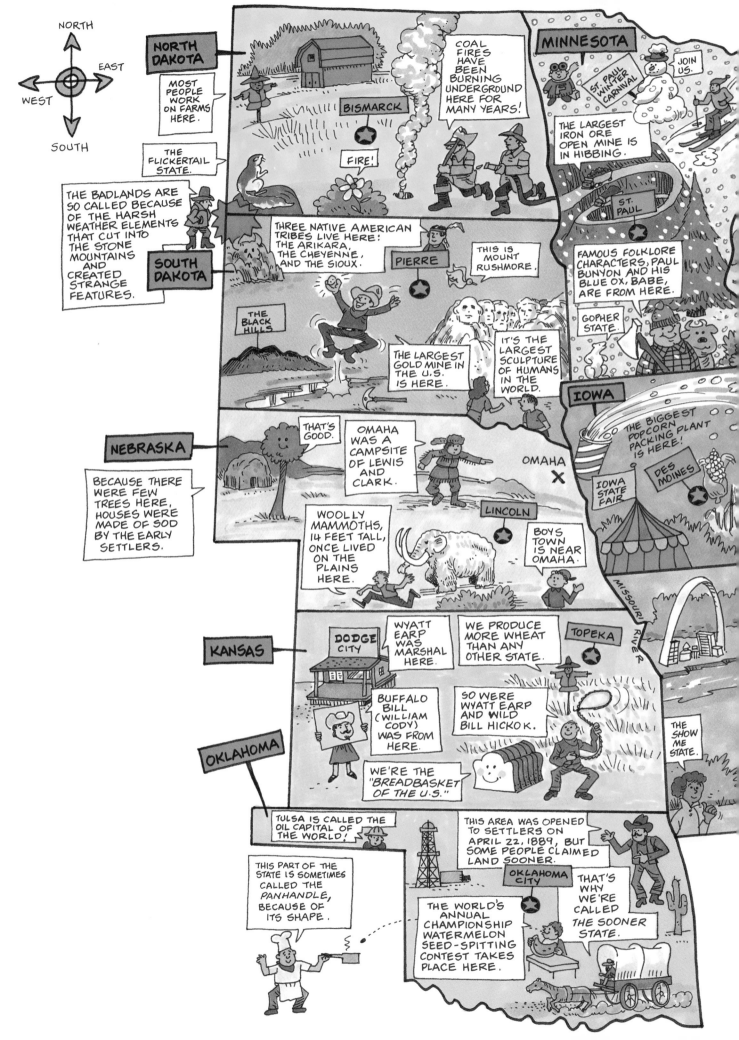

THE U.S.: THE MIDWESTERN STATES

Bordered by the Great Lakes to the north, the Rocky Mountains to the west, and the Appalachian Mountains to the east is a flat, fertile area known as the Great Plains. It produces more than half of the world's corn and enough wheat to make the U.S. the world's largest exporter.

LEARN ABOUT THE U.S.A.'S MIDWESTERN STATES AS YOU LOOK FOR THESE FUN ITEMS:

- ❑ Blue ox
- ❑ Book
- ❑ Cereal
- ❑ Flower
- ❑ Football
- ❑ Heart
- ❑ Race cars (3)
- ❑ Santa Claus
- ❑ Snowman
- ❑ Tire
- ❑ Watermelon slice
- ❑ Woolly mammoth

THE U.S.: THE NORTHEASTERN AND MIDATLANTIC STATES

The most populous region in the country, the northeast and midatlantic states were the first to be settled by Europeans. Colonists arrived from England in 1620 and settled in New Plymouth, Massachusetts.

LEARN ABOUT U.S.A.'S NORTHEASTERN AND MIDATLANTIC STATES AS YOU LOOK FOR THESE FUN ITEMS:

- ❏ Anchor
- ❏ Apple
- ❏ Baseball
- ❏ Basketball
- ❏ Cannon

- ❏ Kite
- ❏ Lighthouse
- ❏ Lobster
- ❏ Ship
- ❏ Skier

- ❏ Treasure chest
- ❏ Truck
- ❏ Umbrella

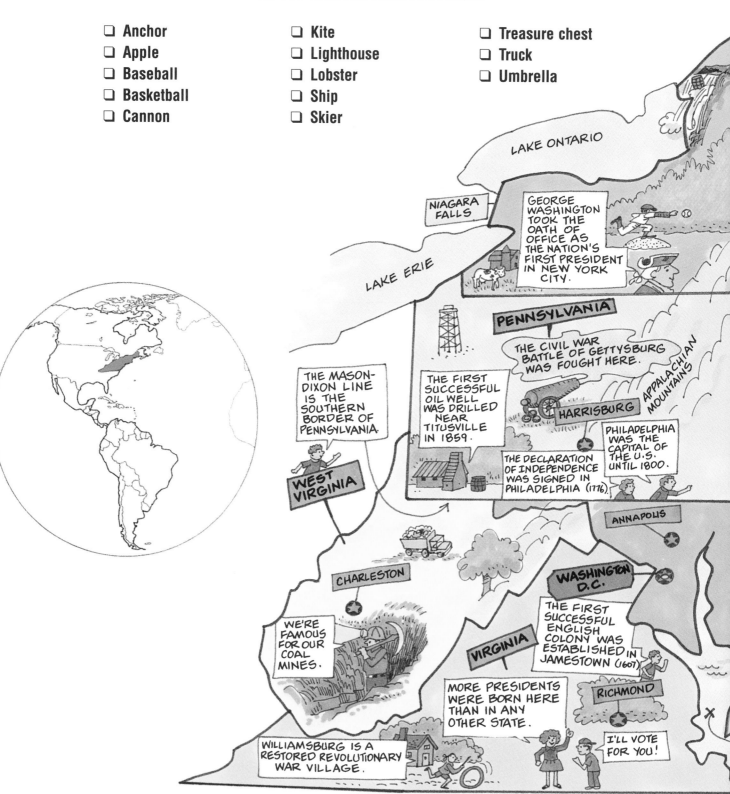

LAKE ONTARIO

NIAGARA FALLS

LAKE ERIE

GEORGE WASHINGTON TOOK THE OATH OF OFFICE AS THE NATION'S FIRST PRESIDENT IN NEW YORK CITY.

PENNSYLVANIA

THE CIVIL WAR BATTLE OF GETTYSBURG WAS FOUGHT HERE.

THE MASON-DIXON LINE IS THE SOUTHERN BORDER OF PENNSYLVANIA.

THE FIRST SUCCESSFUL OIL WELL WAS DRILLED NEAR TITUSVILLE IN 1859.

HARRISBURG

APPALACHIAN MOUNTAINS

PHILADELPHIA WAS THE CAPITAL OF THE U.S. UNTIL 1800.

THE DECLARATION OF INDEPENDENCE WAS SIGNED IN PHILADELPHIA (1776).

WEST VIRGINIA

ANNAPOLIS

CHARLESTON

WASHINGTON D.C.

THE FIRST SUCCESSFUL ENGLISH COLONY WAS ESTABLISHED IN JAMESTOWN (1607)

WE'RE FAMOUS FOR OUR COAL MINES.

VIRGINIA

RICHMOND

MORE PRESIDENTS WERE BORN HERE THAN IN ANY OTHER STATE.

I'LL VOTE FOR YOU!

WILLIAMSBURG IS A RESTORED REVOLUTIONARY WAR VILLAGE.

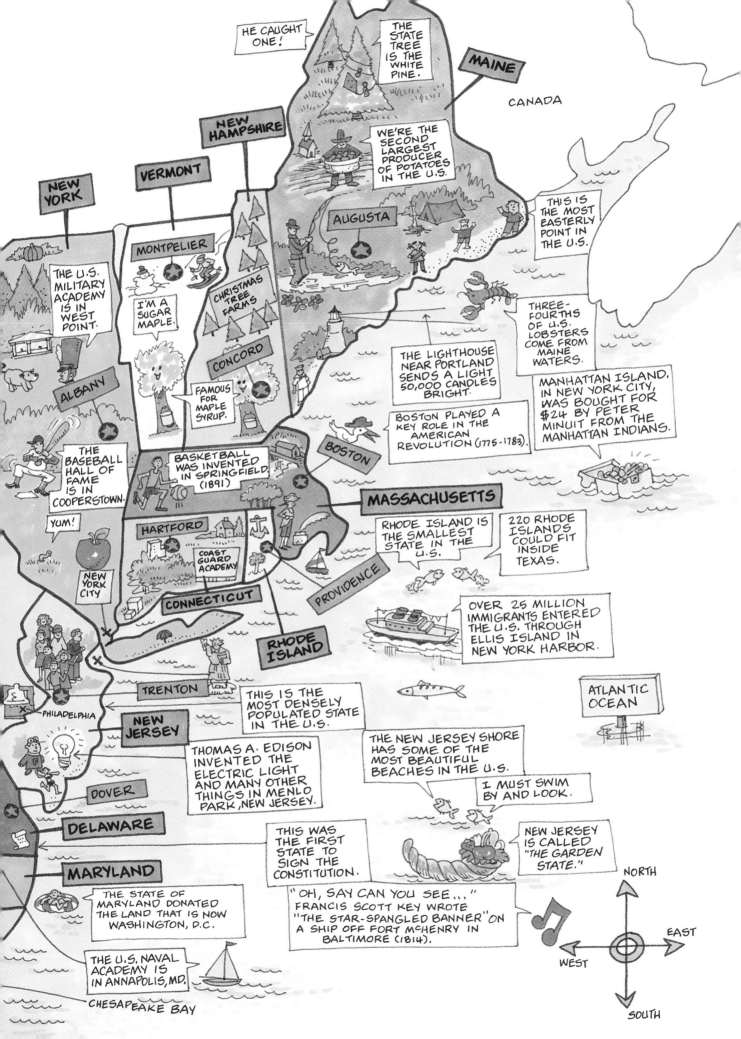

THE U.S.: THE SOUTHERN STATES

The southern states, which extend from the Atlantic coast to Texas, were once totally farm-based, producing mainly cotton and tobacco. Although still agricultural, the area is now strong in industry, and produces oil as well as iron and steel.

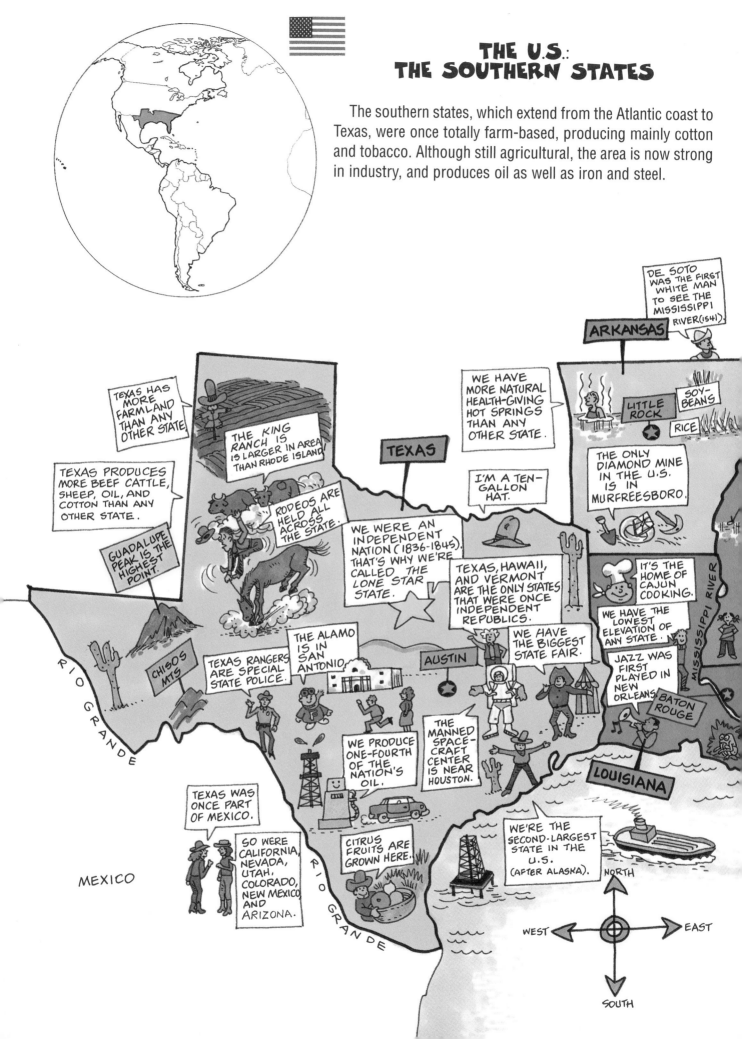

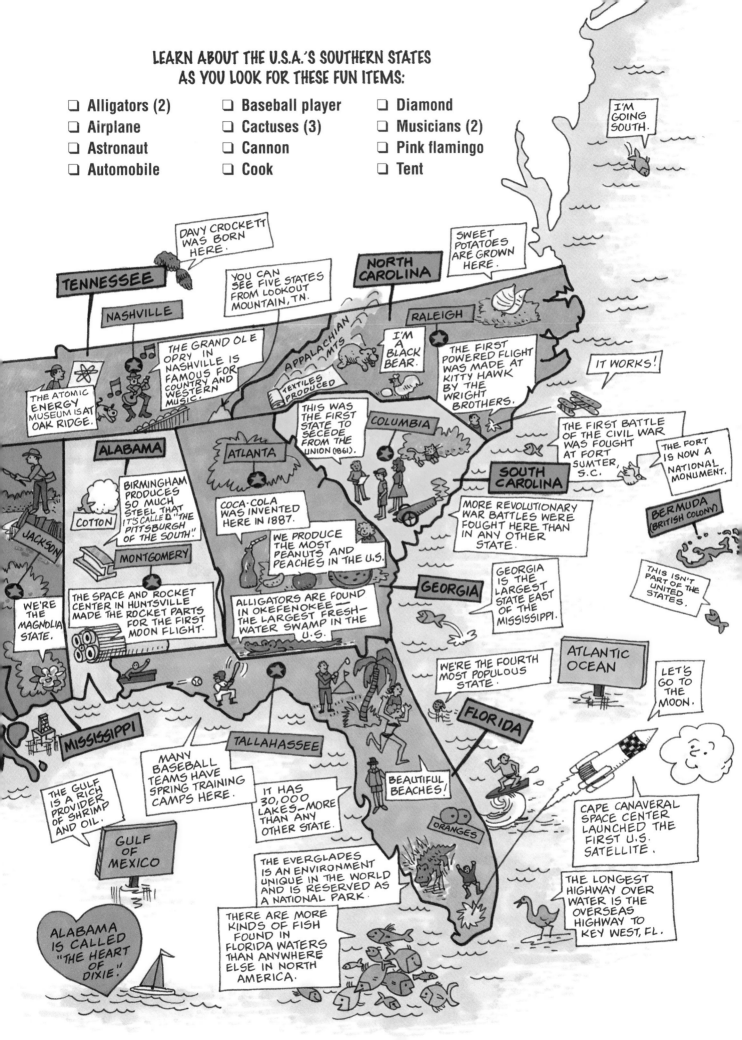

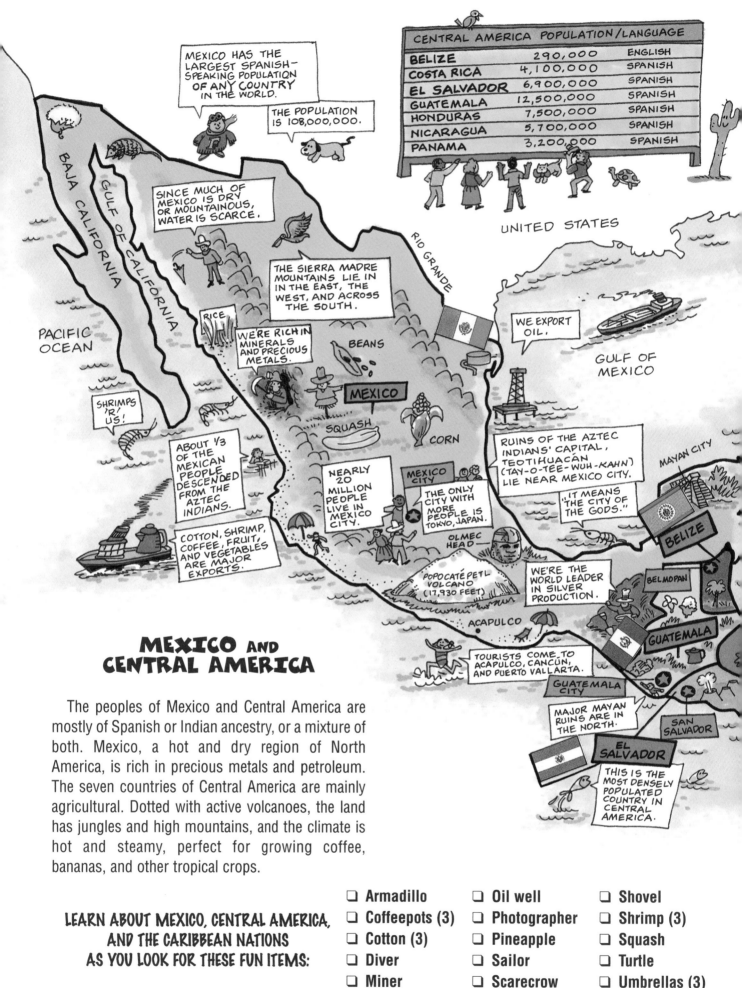

MEXICO AND CENTRAL AMERICA

The peoples of Mexico and Central America are mostly of Spanish or Indian ancestry, or a mixture of both. Mexico, a hot and dry region of North America, is rich in precious metals and petroleum. The seven countries of Central America are mainly agricultural. Dotted with active volcanoes, the land has jungles and high mountains, and the climate is hot and steamy, perfect for growing coffee, bananas, and other tropical crops.

LEARN ABOUT MEXICO, CENTRAL AMERICA, AND THE CARIBBEAN NATIONS AS YOU LOOK FOR THESE FUN ITEMS:

- ❑ Armadillo
- ❑ Coffeepots (3)
- ❑ Cotton (3)
- ❑ Diver
- ❑ Miner
- ❑ Oil well
- ❑ Photographer
- ❑ Pineapple
- ❑ Sailor
- ❑ Scarecrow
- ❑ Shovel
- ❑ Shrimp (3)
- ❑ Squash
- ❑ Turtle
- ❑ Umbrellas (3)

THE CARIBBEAN NATIONS

A chain of tropical islands about 2,000 miles long stretches across the Caribbean Sea, then curves like a hook toward South America. These islands were the first land in the Americas that Christopher Columbus saw and set foot on during his 1492 voyage of discovery. In the 16th century, Europeans colonized the islands, bringing African slaves to work plantations.

Today, 13 of the islands or island groups are independent nations (see list below). Others are territories of the U.S. or European countries. Most of the people living here are descendants of African slaves, Spanish conquerors, or both. Most countries in this region depend on tourism and agriculture for their income.

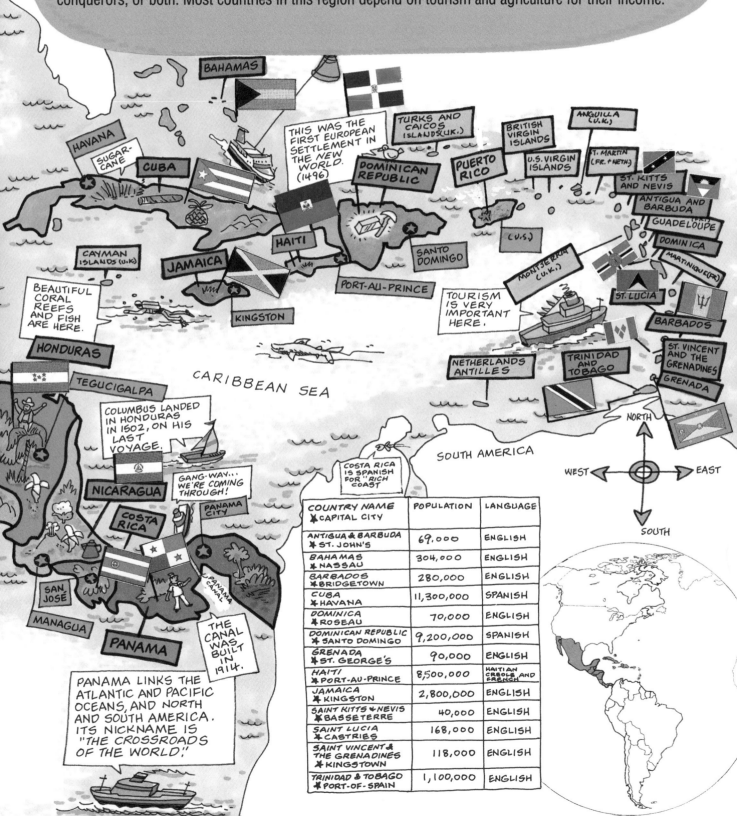

COUNTRY NAME ✹ CAPITAL CITY	POPULATION	LANGUAGE
ANTIGUA & BARBUDA ✹ ST. JOHN'S	69,000	ENGLISH
BAHAMAS ✹ NASSAU	304,000	ENGLISH
BARBADOS ✹ BRIDGETOWN	280,000	ENGLISH
CUBA ✹ HAVANA	11,300,000	SPANISH
DOMINICA ✹ ROSEAU	70,000	ENGLISH
DOMINICAN REPUBLIC ✹ SANTO DOMINGO	9,200,000	SPANISH
GRENADA ✹ ST. GEORGE'S	90,000	ENGLISH
HAITI ✹ PORT-AU-PRINCE	8,500,000	HAITIAN CREOLE AND FRENCH
JAMAICA ✹ KINGSTON	2,800,000	ENGLISH
SAINT KITTS & NEVIS ✹ BASSETERRE	40,000	ENGLISH
SAINT LUCIA ✹ CASTRIES	168,000	ENGLISH
SAINT VINCENT & THE GRENADINES ✹ KINGSTOWN	118,000	ENGLISH
TRINIDAD & TOBAGO ✹ PORT-OF-SPAIN	1,100,000	ENGLISH

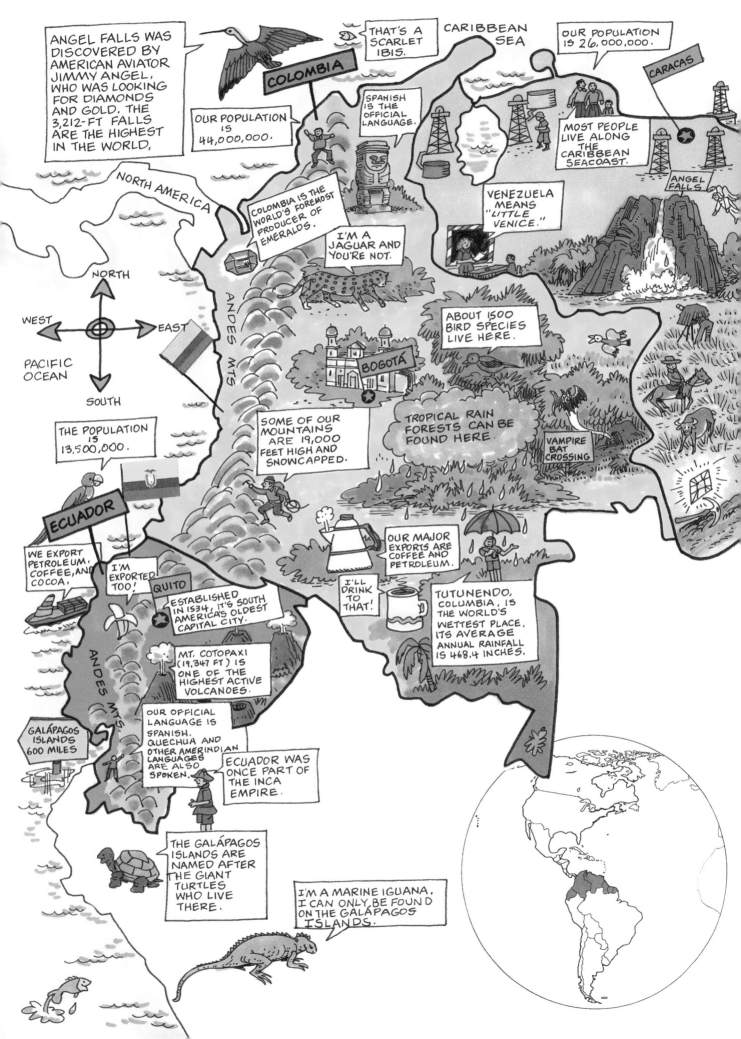

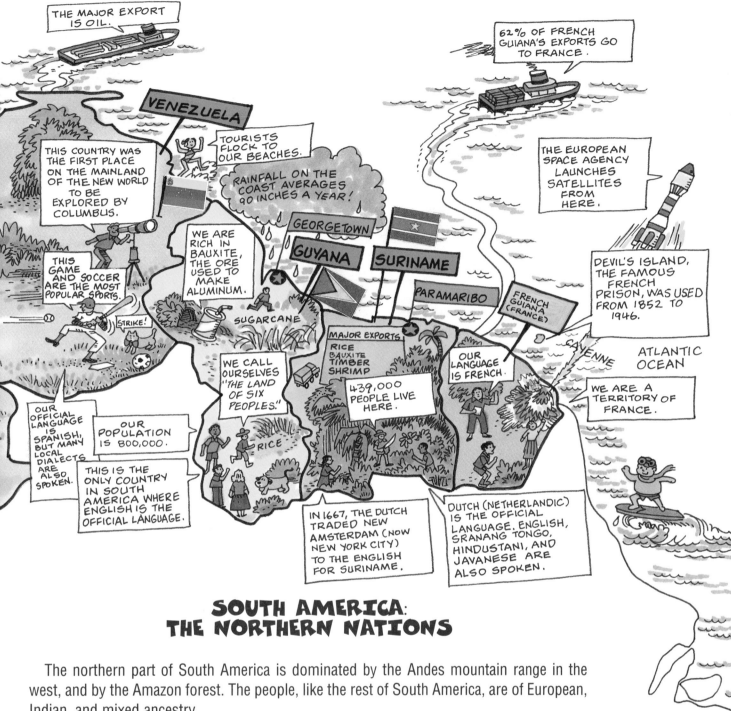

SOUTH AMERICA: THE NORTHERN NATIONS

The northern part of South America is dominated by the Andes mountain range in the west, and by the Amazon forest. The people, like the rest of South America, are of European, Indian, and mixed ancestry.

Once Spanish colonies, Ecuador, Colombia, and Venezuela won their independence in the early decades of the 19th century. Guyana and Suriname gained their independence only recently: Guyana in 1966, from Britain; and Suriname in 1975, from the Netherlands. French Guiana is the only country on the South American mainland that is still a European territory.

LEARN ABOUT SOUTH AMERICA'S NORTHERN NATIONS AS YOU LOOK FOR THESE FUN ITEMS:

- ❏ Aluminum can
- ❏ Angel
- ❏ Baseball bat
- ❏ Cup
- ❏ Emerald
- ❏ Flying bat
- ❏ Ibis
- ❏ Iguana
- ❏ Jaguar
- ❏ Mountain climber
- ❏ Photographer
- ❏ Satellite rocket
- ❏ Schoolteacher
- ❏ Soccer ball
- ❏ Stone idol
- ❏ Surfer
- ❏ Telescope
- ❏ Turtle

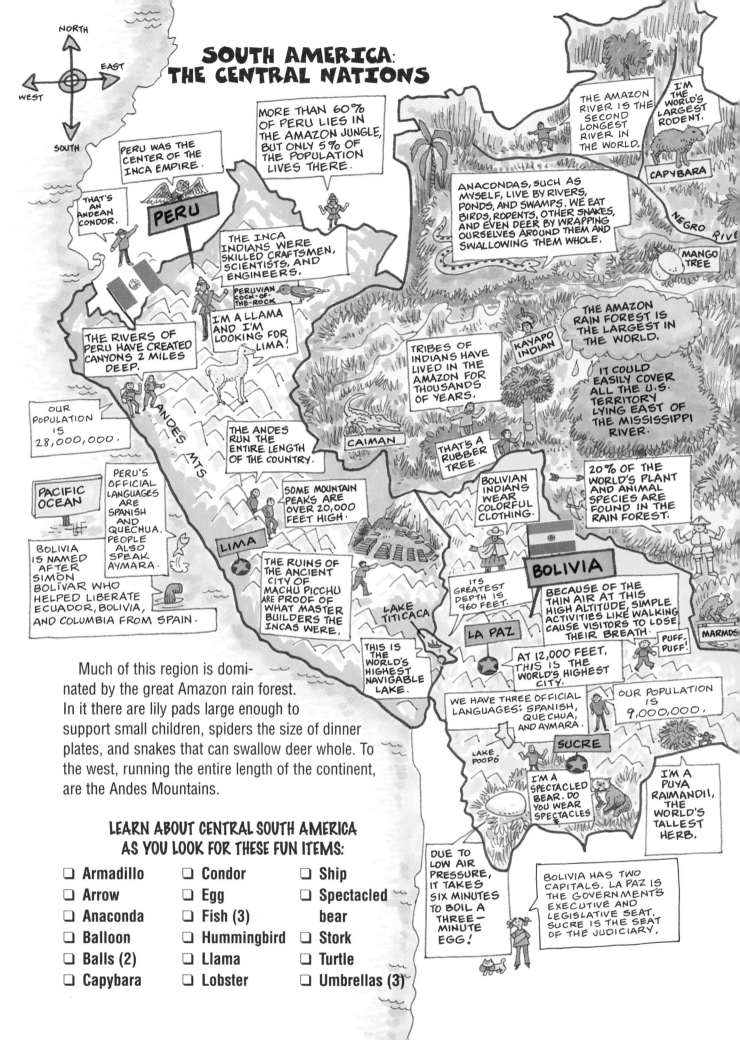

SOUTH AMERICA: THE CENTRAL NATIONS

NORTH
EAST
WEST
SOUTH

PERU WAS THE CENTER OF THE INCA EMPIRE.

MORE THAN 60% OF PERU LIES IN THE AMAZON JUNGLE, BUT ONLY 5% OF THE POPULATION LIVES THERE.

THAT'S AN ANDEAN CONDOR.

PERU

THE INCA INDIANS WERE SKILLED CRAFTSMEN, SCIENTISTS, AND ENGINEERS.

PERUVIAN COCK-OF-THE-ROCK

I'M A LLAMA AND I'M LOOKING FOR LIMA!

THE RIVERS OF PERU HAVE CREATED CANYONS 2 MILES DEEP.

OUR POPULATION IS 28,000,000.

ANDES MTS.

THE ANDES RUN THE ENTIRE LENGTH OF THE COUNTRY.

PACIFIC OCEAN

PERU'S OFFICIAL LANGUAGES ARE SPANISH AND QUECHUA. PEOPLE ALSO SPEAK AYMARA.

BOLIVIA IS NAMED AFTER SIMON BOLIVAR WHO HELPED LIBERATE ECUADOR, BOLIVIA, AND COLUMBIA FROM SPAIN.

LIMA

SOME MOUNTAIN PEAKS ARE OVER 20,000 FEET HIGH.

THE RUINS OF THE ANCIENT CITY OF MACHU PICCHU ARE PROOF OF WHAT MASTER BUILDERS THE INCAS WERE.

THE AMAZON RIVER IS THE SECOND LONGEST RIVER IN THE WORLD.

I'M THE WORLD'S LARGEST RODENT.

CAPYBARA

NEGRO RIVER

ANACONDAS, SUCH AS MYSELF, LIVE BY RIVERS, PONDS, AND SWAMPS. WE EAT BIRDS, RODENTS, OTHER SNAKES, AND EVEN DEER BY WRAPPING OURSELVES AROUND THEM AND SWALLOWING THEM WHOLE.

MANGO TREE

THE AMAZON RAIN FOREST IS THE LARGEST IN THE WORLD.

IT COULD EASILY COVER ALL THE U.S. TERRITORY LYING EAST OF THE MISSISSIPPI RIVER.

KAYAPO INDIAN

TRIBES OF INDIANS HAVE LIVED IN THE AMAZON FOR THOUSANDS OF YEARS.

CAIMAN

THAT'S A RUBBER TREE.

BOLIVIAN INDIANS WEAR COLORFUL CLOTHING.

20% OF THE WORLD'S PLANT AND ANIMAL SPECIES ARE FOUND IN THE RAIN FOREST.

BOLIVIA

ITS GREATEST DEPTH IS 960 FEET.

BECAUSE OF THE THIN AIR AT THIS HIGH ALTITUDE, SIMPLE ACTIVITIES LIKE WALKING CAUSE VISITORS TO LOSE THEIR BREATH.

PUFF! PUFF!

MARMOS

LAKE TITICACA

THIS IS THE WORLD'S HIGHEST NAVIGABLE LAKE.

LA PAZ

AT 12,000 FEET, THIS IS THE WORLD'S HIGHEST CITY.

WE HAVE THREE OFFICIAL LANGUAGES: SPANISH, QUECHUA, AND AYMARA.

OUR POPULATION IS 9,000,000.

SUCRE

LAKE POOPÓ

I'M A SPECTACLED BEAR. DO YOU WEAR SPECTACLES?

I'M A PUYA RAIMANDII, THE WORLD'S TALLEST HERB.

DUE TO LOW AIR PRESSURE, IT TAKES SIX MINUTES TO BOIL A THREE-MINUTE EGG!

BOLIVIA HAS TWO CAPITALS. LA PAZ IS THE GOVERNMENTS EXECUTIVE AND LEGISLATIVE SEAT. SUCRE IS THE SEAT OF THE JUDICIARY.

Much of this region is dominated by the great Amazon rain forest. In it there are lily pads large enough to support small children, spiders the size of dinner plates, and snakes that can swallow deer whole. To the west, running the entire length of the continent, are the Andes Mountains.

LEARN ABOUT CENTRAL SOUTH AMERICA AS YOU LOOK FOR THESE FUN ITEMS:

- ☐ Armadillo
- ☐ Arrow
- ☐ Anaconda
- ☐ Balloon
- ☐ Balls (2)
- ☐ Capybara
- ☐ Condor
- ☐ Egg
- ☐ Fish (3)
- ☐ Hummingbird
- ☐ Llama
- ☐ Lobster
- ☐ Ship
- ☐ Spectacled bear
- ☐ Stork
- ☐ Turtle
- ☐ Umbrellas (3)

SOUTH AMERICA: THE SOUTHERN NATIONS

The southern region of South America has various types of landscapes, including grassy plains, deserts, mountains, forests, and frozen glaciers. It is a region rich in natural resources.

LEARN ABOUT SOUTH AMERICA'S SOUTHERN NATIONS AS YOU LOOK FOR THESE FUN ITEMS:

☐ Albatross
☐ Anteater
☐ Ball
☐ Boat
☐ Dancers
☐ Grapes

PARAGUAY

THE QUEBRACHO TREE, CALLED THE "AXE BREAKER," IS SO DENSE AND HEAVY THAT THE WOOD SINKS IN WATER.

OUR POPULATION IS 6,500,000.

THE PARANÁ RIVER DIVIDES THIS LANDLOCKED COUNTRY.

THE OLD CAPITAL IS KNOWN FOR ITS PARKS, PUBLIC GARDENS, AND FLOWERING TREES.

ORANGES

OUR CHIEF CROPS ARE COTTON, SUGARCANE, AND CORN.

ASUNCIÓN

MOST PARAGUAYANS ARE PART GUARANI INDIAN AND PART SPANISH. BOTH LANGUAGES ARE SPOKEN.

THE WEST IS A DRY GRASSLAND WHERE CATTLE GRAZE ON LARGE RANCHES.

I'M A GAUCHO.

THAT'S A CATTLE HERDER.

COTTON

WOULD YOU LIKE A CUP OF YMATE'?

IT'S A TYPE OF TEA.

URUGUAY

OUR POPULATION IS 3,450,000.

OFFICIAL LANGUAGE IS SPANISH.

IN SPRING, A PURPLE FLOWER BLOOMS, GIVING US THE NICKNAME OF "THE PURPLE LAND."

MONTEVIDEO

BEAUTIFUL BEACHES!

URUGUAY RIVER

PARANÁ RIVER

ARGENTINA

I'M A GIANT ANTEATER.

I HAVEN'T SEEN ANY GIANT ANTS!

THE ANDES MOUNTAINS RUN LIKE A SPINE DOWN THE CHILE-ARGENTINE BORDER.

OUR POPULATION IS 40,000,000.

POLO IS POPULAR HERE.

OJOS DEL SALADO (22,614 FT.) IS THE WORLD'S HIGHEST ACTIVE VOLCANO.

ARGENTINA IS THE SECOND-LARGEST COUNTRY IN S.A. IT IS ABOUT ONE-THIRD THE SIZE OF THE U.S.

97% OF THE POPULATION IS OF EUROPEAN ANCESTRY.

BUENOS AIRES

PAMPAS

SUGARCANE

THIS IS A FERTILE GRASSY PLAIN WHERE CATTLE ARE RAISED.

ANDES MOUNTAINS

CHERRIES

CHILE

THE DESERT IS VERY DRY, BUT VERY RICH IN COPPER, GOLD, AND SILVER.

OUR POPULATION IS 16,200,000.

LICANCÁBUR VOLCANO (19,425 FT.)

ATACAMA DESERT

CHILE IS ONLY 217 MILES ACROSS AT ITS WIDEST POINT, BUT 2,700 MILES LONG FROM ITS PERU BORDER TO CAPE HORN.

THE ATACAMA DESERT IS EARTH'S DRIEST PLACE.

RAIN FELL IN THE ATACAMA DESERT IN 1971 FOR THE FIRST TIME IN 400 YEARS.

IT'S A LONG WAIT.

THAT BIRD'S A CONDOR.

MT. ACONCAGUA (22,834 FT.) IS THE HIGHEST PEAK IN THE WORLD OUTSIDE OF THOSE IN ASIA.

SANTIAGO

WINE MAKING IS A MAJOR INDUSTRY.

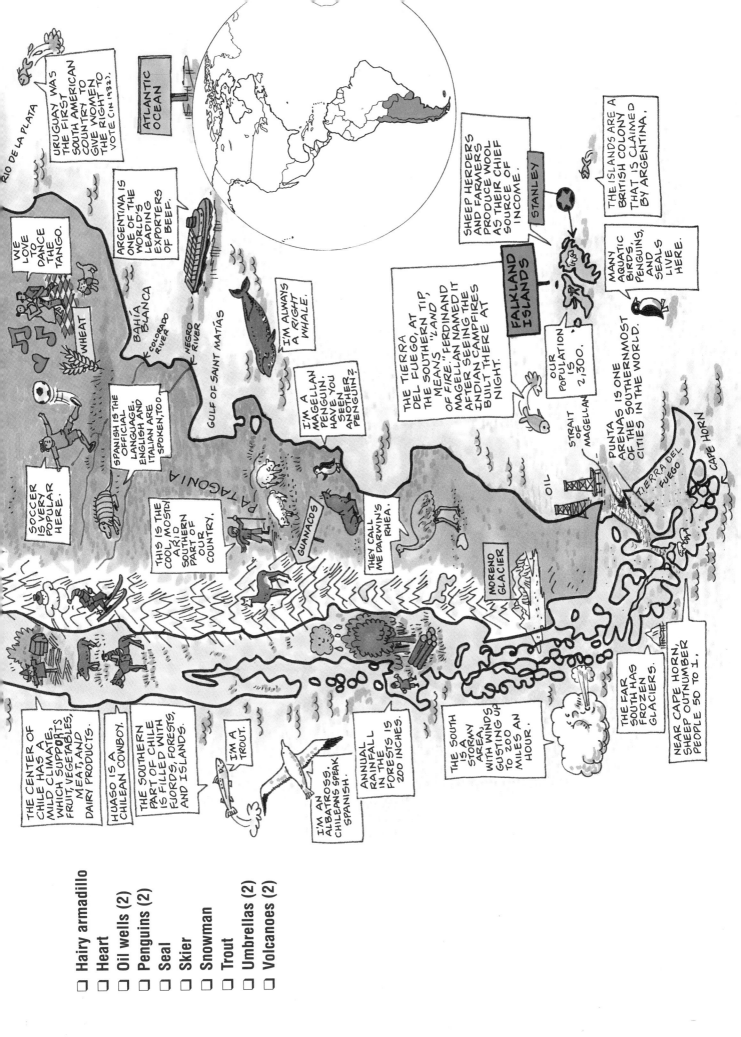

EUROPE

The seat of Western civilization, Europe has had a strong influence on the world through trade, exploration, and industry.

The continent stretches from the icy Arctic Circle in the north to the warm Mediterranean Sea in the south. Its western border is the North Atlantic Ocean and its eastern borders are the Ural and Caucasus mountains. The land—with its fertile plains and tall mountains—is as varied as its countries, peoples, and cultures.

LEARN ABOUT EUROPE AS YOU LOOK FOR THESE FUN ITEMS:

- ❏ Cyclist
- ❏ Eiffel Tower
- ❏ Fish (3)
- ❏ Grapes
- ❏ Puffin
- ❏ Sailboat
- ❏ Volcano
- ❏ Windmill
- ❏ Wooden shoe

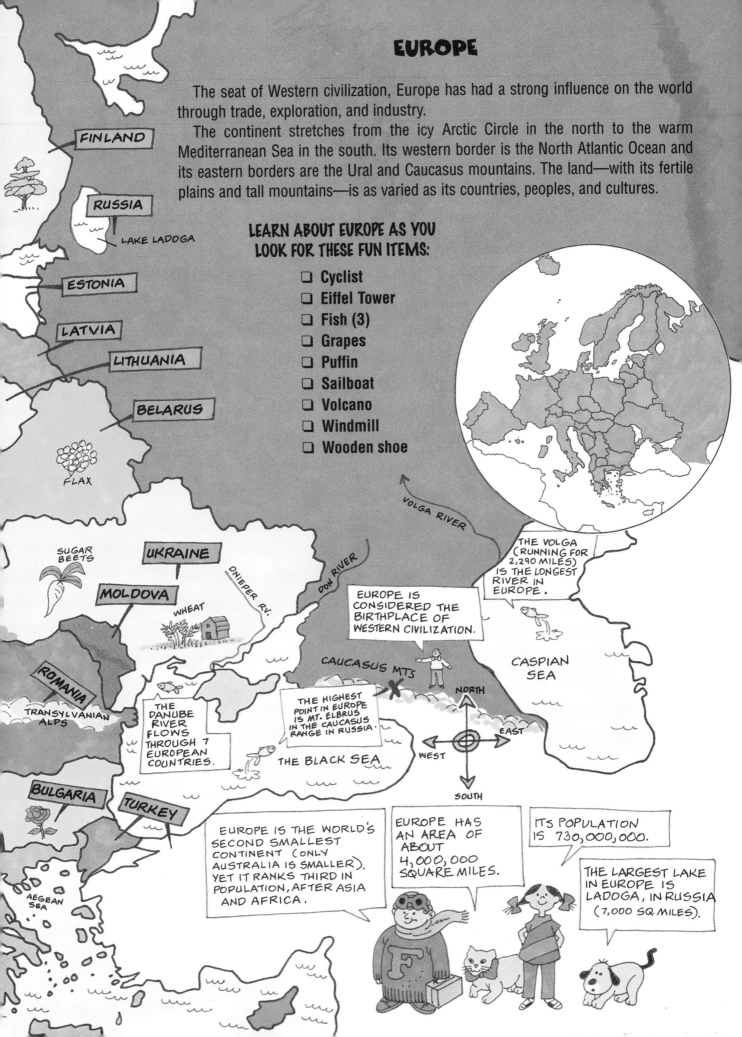

FINLAND

RUSSIA

LAKE LADOGA

ESTONIA

LATVIA

LITHUANIA

BELARUS

FLAX

VOLGA RIVER

THE VOLGA (RUNNING FOR 2,290 MILES) IS THE LONGEST RIVER IN EUROPE.

SUGAR BEETS

UKRAINE

MOLDOVA

WHEAT

DNIEPER RV.

DON RIVER

EUROPE IS CONSIDERED THE BIRTHPLACE OF WESTERN CIVILIZATION.

CASPIAN SEA

ROMANIA

TRANSYLVANIAN ALPS

THE DANUBE RIVER FLOWS THROUGH 7 EUROPEAN COUNTRIES.

CAUCASUS MTS

THE HIGHEST POINT IN EUROPE IS MT. ELBRUS IN THE CAUCASUS RANGE IN RUSSIA.

THE BLACK SEA

NORTH

EAST

WEST

SOUTH

BULGARIA

TURKEY

AEGEAN SEA

EUROPE IS THE WORLD'S SECOND SMALLEST CONTINENT (ONLY AUSTRALIA IS SMALLER). YET IT RANKS THIRD IN POPULATION, AFTER ASIA AND AFRICA.

EUROPE HAS AN AREA OF ABOUT 4,000,000 SQUARE MILES.

ITS POPULATION IS 730,000,000.

THE LARGEST LAKE IN EUROPE IS LADOGA, IN RUSSIA (7,000 SQ. MILES).

United Kingdom and Ireland

The United Kingdom is a country made up of four parts: England, Wales, Scotland, and Northern Ireland. (The first three are also known as Britain.) Northern Ireland is on the same large island as the independent country of Ireland. In the late 19th and early 20th centuries, Great Britain was the world's leading industrial and trading nation. Its worldwide empire included Canada, India, Australia, New Zealand, and parts of Africa.

LEARN ABOUT THE UNITED KINGDOM AND IRELAND AS YOU LOOK FOR THESE FUN ITEMS:

- ☐ Bagpipe
- ☐ Big Ben
- ☐ Bus
- ☐ Deer
- ☐ Ferry
- ☐ Four-leaf clover
- ☐ Golf
- ☐ Knight in armor
- ☐ Lobster
- ☐ "Nessie"
- ☐ Sheep (3)
- ☐ Soccer ball
- ☐ Tennis racket

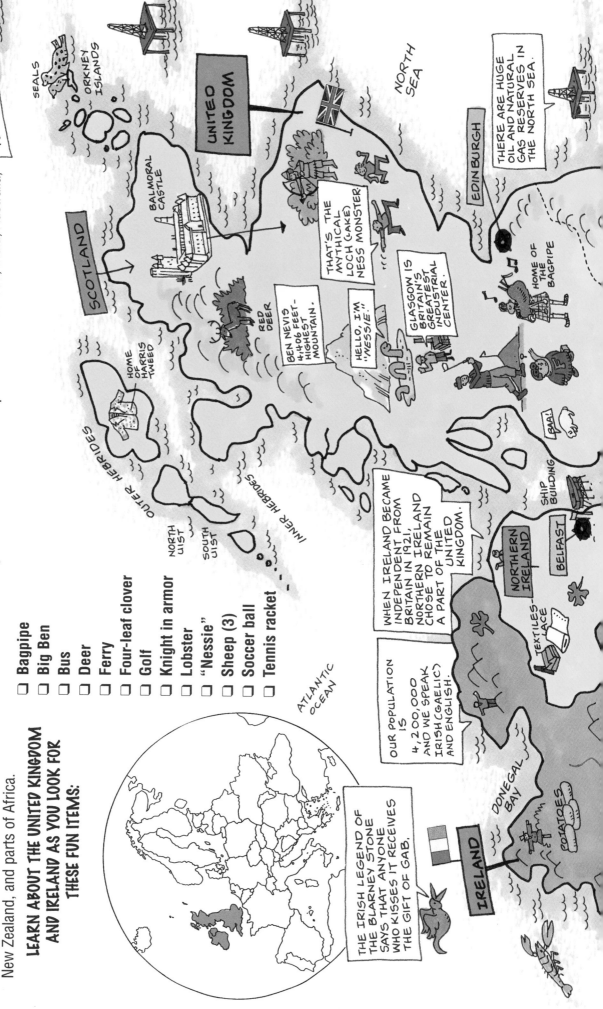

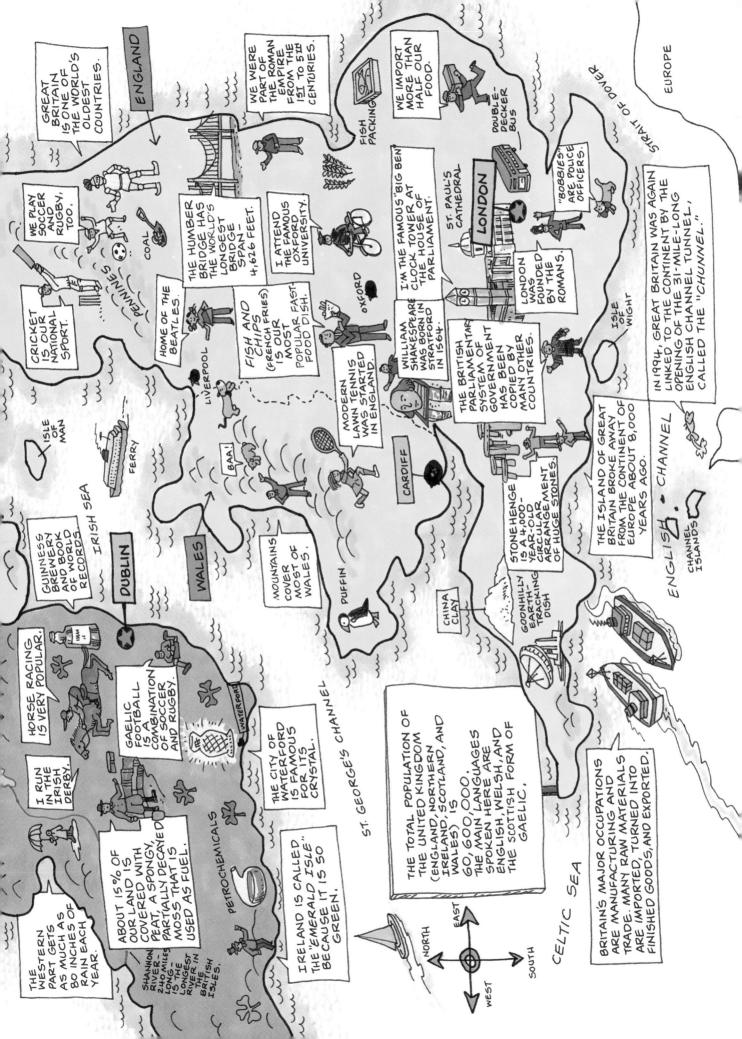

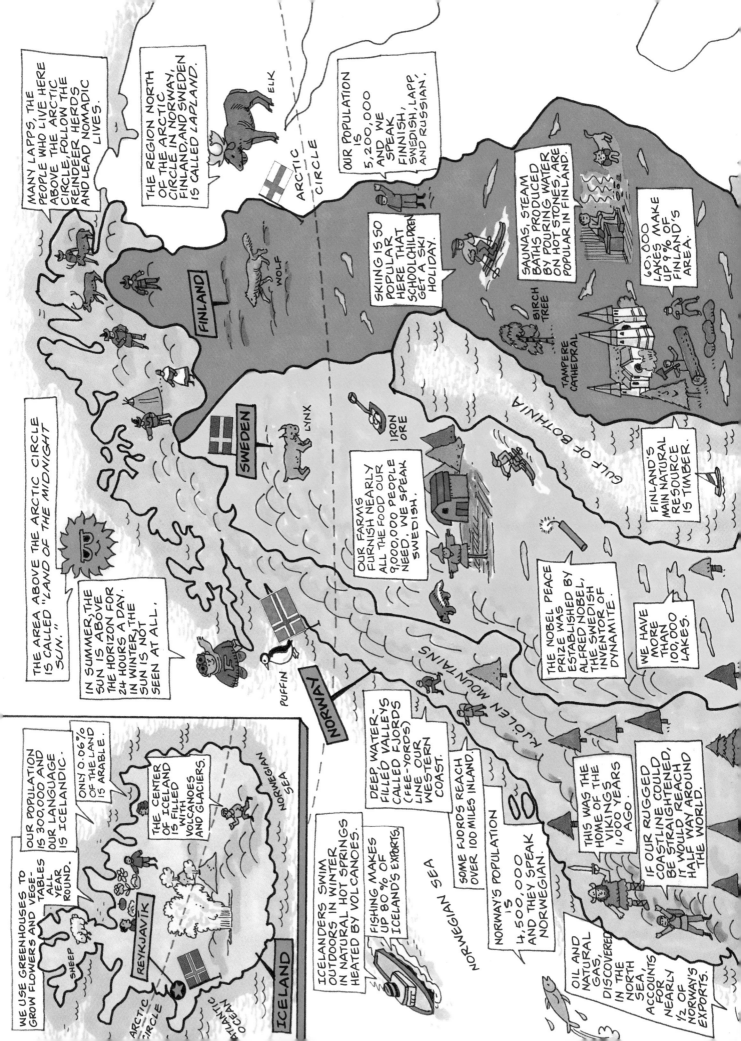

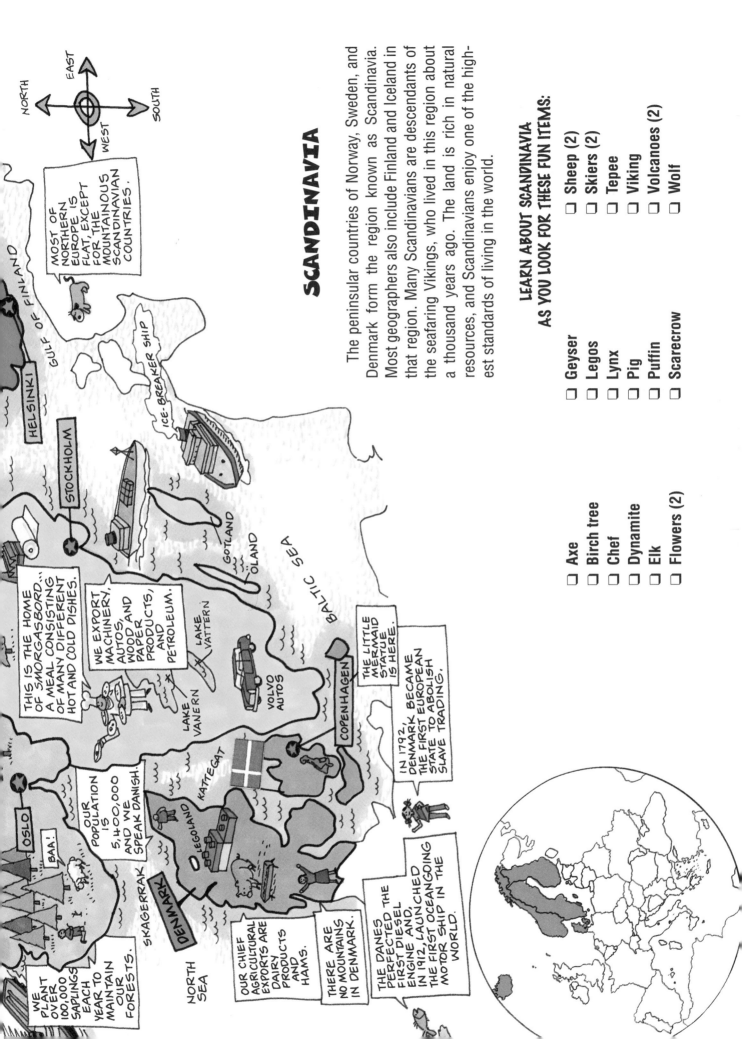

NORTH

EAST

WEST

SOUTH

SCANDINAVIA

The peninsular countries of Norway, Sweden, and Denmark form the region known as Scandinavia. Most geographers also include Finland and Iceland in that region. Many Scandinavians are descendants of the seafaring Vikings, who lived in this region about a thousand years ago. The land is rich in natural resources, and Scandinavians enjoy one of the highest standards of living in the world.

LEARN ABOUT SCANDINAVIA
AS YOU LOOK FOR THESE FUN ITEMS:

- ☐ Axe
- ☐ Birch tree
- ☐ Chef
- ☐ Dynamite
- ☐ Elk
- ☐ Flowers (2)

- ☐ Geyser
- ☐ Legos
- ☐ Lynx
- ☐ Pig
- ☐ Puffin
- ☐ Scarecrow

- ☐ Sheep (2)
- ☐ Skiers (2)
- ☐ Tepee
- ☐ Viking
- ☐ Volcanoes (2)
- ☐ Wolf

MOST OF NORTHERN EUROPE IS FLAT, EXCEPT FOR THE MOUNTAINOUS SCANDINAVIAN COUNTRIES.

GULF OF FINLAND

HELSINKI

ICE-BREAKER SHIP

STOCKHOLM

GOTLAND

ÖLAND

BALTIC SEA

THIS IS THE HOME OF SMORGASBORD... A MEAL CONSISTING OF MANY DIFFERENT HOT AND COLD DISHES.

WE EXPORT MACHINERY, AUTOS, WOOD AND PAPER PRODUCTS, AND PETROLEUM.

LAKE VÄTTERN

LAKE VÄNERN

VOLVO AUTOS

COPENHAGEN

THE LITTLE MERMAID STATUE IS HERE.

IN 1792, DENMARK BECAME THE FIRST EUROPEAN STATE TO ABOLISH SLAVE TRADING.

KATTEGAT

LEGOLAND

OSLO

BAA!

OUR POPULATION IS 5,400,000 AND WE SPEAK DANISH.

SKAGERRAK

DENMARK

NORTH SEA

OUR CHIEF AGRICULTURAL EXPORTS ARE DAIRY PRODUCTS AND HAMS.

THERE ARE NO MOUNTAINS IN DENMARK.

THE DANES PERFECTED THE FIRST DIESEL ENGINE AND, IN 1912, LAUNCHED THE FIRST OCEANGOING MOTOR SHIP IN THE WORLD.

WE PLANT OVER 100,000 SAPLINGS EACH YEAR TO MAINTAIN OUR FORESTS.

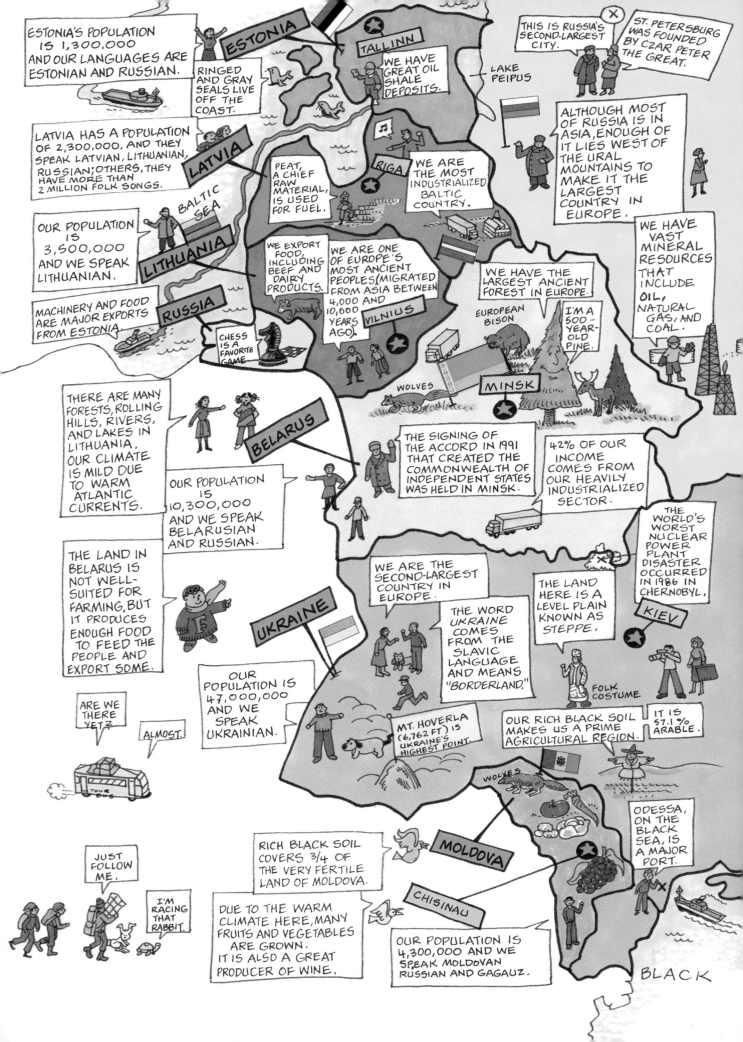

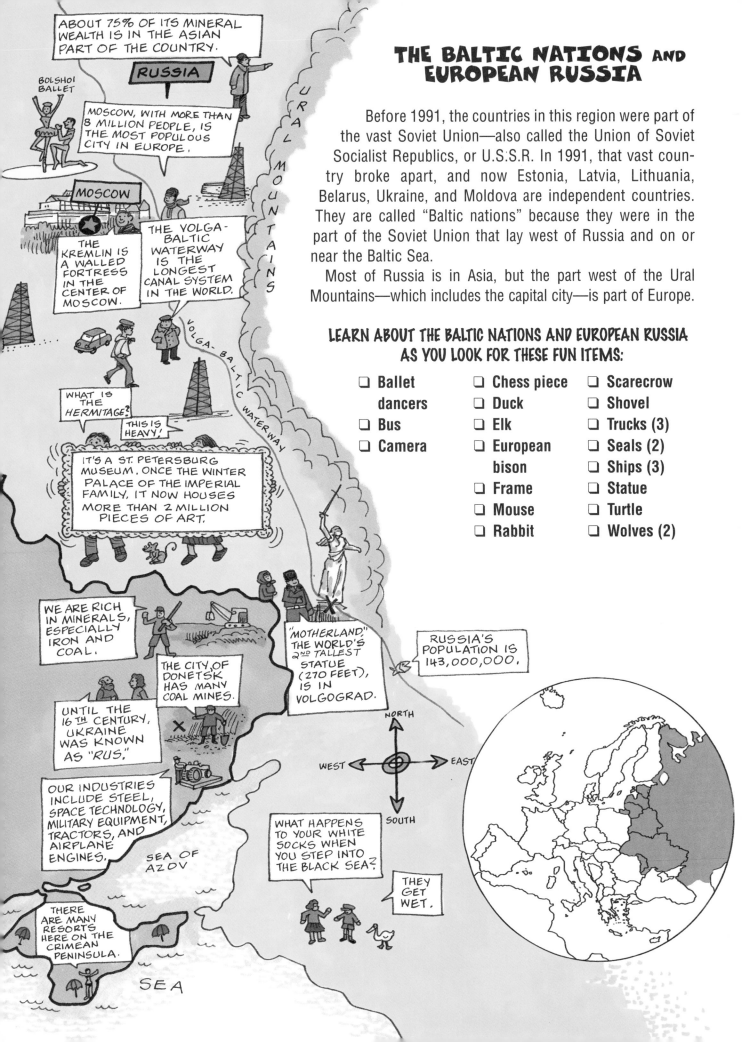

THE BALTIC NATIONS AND EUROPEAN RUSSIA

Before 1991, the countries in this region were part of the vast Soviet Union—also called the Union of Soviet Socialist Republics, or U.S.S.R. In 1991, that vast country broke apart, and now Estonia, Latvia, Lithuania, Belarus, Ukraine, and Moldova are independent countries. They are called "Baltic nations" because they were in the part of the Soviet Union that lay west of Russia and on or near the Baltic Sea.

Most of Russia is in Asia, but the part west of the Ural Mountains—which includes the capital city—is part of Europe.

LEARN ABOUT THE BALTIC NATIONS AND EUROPEAN RUSSIA AS YOU LOOK FOR THESE FUN ITEMS:

- ❏ Ballet dancers
- ❏ Bus
- ❏ Camera
- ❏ Chess piece
- ❏ Duck
- ❏ Elk
- ❏ European bison
- ❏ Frame
- ❏ Mouse
- ❏ Rabbit
- ❏ Scarecrow
- ❏ Shovel
- ❏ Trucks (3)
- ❏ Seals (2)
- ❏ Ships (3)
- ❏ Statue
- ❏ Turtle
- ❏ Wolves (2)

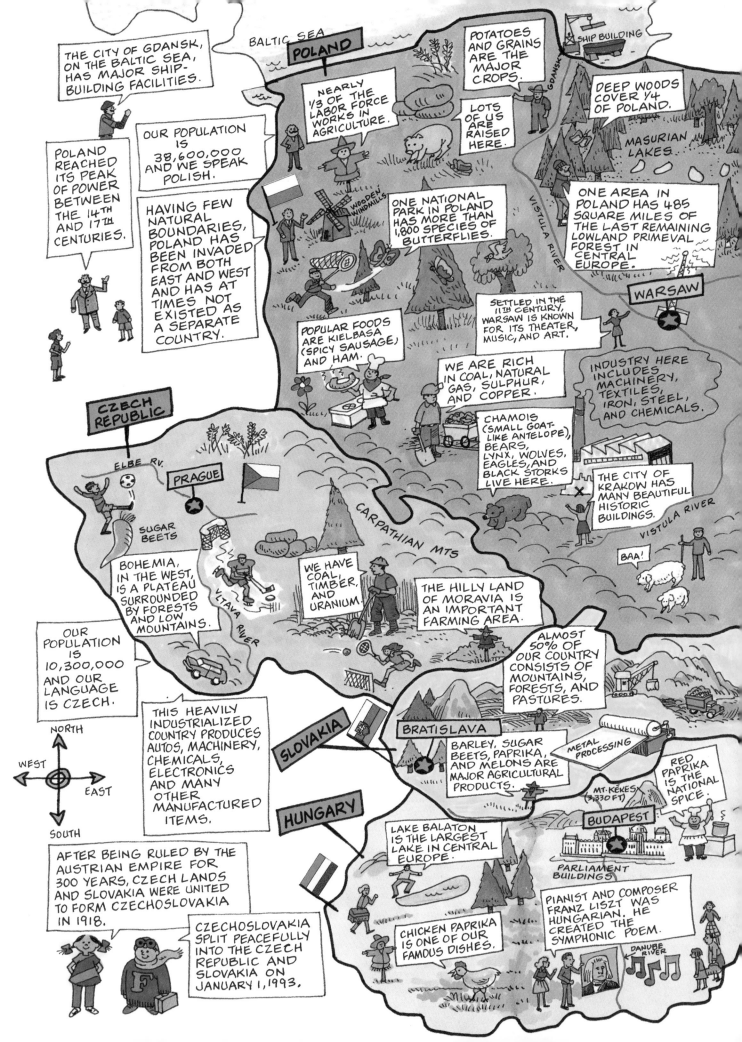

BALTIC SEA

POLAND

THE CITY OF GDANSK, ON THE BALTIC SEA, HAS MAJOR SHIP-BUILDING FACILITIES.

NEARLY 1/3 OF THE LABOR FORCE WORKS IN AGRICULTURE.

POTATOES AND GRAINS ARE THE MAJOR CROPS.

SHIP BUILDING

LOTS OF US ARE RAISED HERE.

DEEP WOODS COVER 1/4 OF POLAND.

MASURIAN LAKES

POLAND REACHED ITS PEAK OF POWER BETWEEN THE 14TH AND 17TH CENTURIES.

OUR POPULATION IS 38,600,000 AND WE SPEAK POLISH.

HAVING FEW NATURAL BOUNDARIES, POLAND HAS BEEN INVADED FROM BOTH EAST AND WEST AND HAS AT TIMES NOT EXISTED AS A SEPARATE COUNTRY.

WOODEN WINDMILLS

ONE NATIONAL PARK IN POLAND HAS MORE THAN 1,800 SPECIES OF BUTTERFLIES.

VISTULA RIVER

ONE AREA IN POLAND HAS 485 SQUARE MILES OF THE LAST REMAINING LOWLAND PRIMEVAL FOREST IN CENTRAL EUROPE.

WARSAW

SETTLED IN THE 11TH CENTURY, WARSAW IS KNOWN FOR ITS THEATER, MUSIC, AND ART.

POPULAR FOODS ARE KIELBASA (SPICY SAUSAGE) AND HAM.

WE ARE RICH IN COAL, NATURAL GAS, SULPHUR, AND COPPER.

INDUSTRY HERE INCLUDES MACHINERY, TEXTILES, IRON, STEEL, AND CHEMICALS.

CZECH REPUBLIC

ELBE RV.

PRAGUE

CHAMOIS (SMALL GOAT-LIKE ANTELOPE), BEARS, LYNX, WOLVES, EAGLES, AND BLACK STORKS LIVE HERE.

CARPATHIAN MTS

THE CITY OF KRAKOW HAS MANY BEAUTIFUL HISTORIC BUILDINGS.

VISTULA RIVER

BAA!

SUGAR BEETS

BOHEMIA, IN THE WEST, IS A PLATEAU SURROUNDED BY FORESTS AND LOW MOUNTAINS.

VLTAVA RIVER

WE HAVE COAL, TIMBER, AND URANIUM.

THE HILLY LAND OF MORAVIA IS AN IMPORTANT FARMING AREA.

ALMOST 50% OF OUR COUNTRY CONSISTS OF MOUNTAINS, FORESTS, AND PASTURES.

OUR POPULATION IS 10,300,000 AND OUR LANGUAGE IS CZECH.

NORTH
WEST
EAST
SOUTH

THIS HEAVILY INDUSTRIALIZED COUNTRY PRODUCES AUTOS, MACHINERY, CHEMICALS, ELECTRONICS AND MANY OTHER MANUFACTURED ITEMS.

SLOVAKIA

BRATISLAVA

METAL PROCESSING

RED PAPRIKA IS THE NATIONAL SPICE.

BARLEY, SUGAR BEETS, PAPRIKA, AND MELONS ARE MAJOR AGRICULTURAL PRODUCTS.

MT. KÉKES (3,330 FT)

BUDAPEST

HUNGARY

LAKE BALATON IS THE LARGEST LAKE IN CENTRAL EUROPE.

PARLIAMENT BUILDINGS

AFTER BEING RULED BY THE AUSTRIAN EMPIRE FOR 300 YEARS, CZECH LANDS AND SLOVAKIA WERE UNITED TO FORM CZECHOSLOVAKIA IN 1918.

CZECHOSLOVAKIA SPLIT PEACEFULLY INTO THE CZECH REPUBLIC AND SLOVAKIA ON JANUARY 1, 1993.

CHICKEN PAPRIKA IS ONE OF OUR FAMOUS DISHES.

PIANIST AND COMPOSER FRANZ LISZT WAS HUNGARIAN. HE CREATED THE SYMPHONIC POEM.

DANUBE RIVER

POLAND, CZECH REPUBLIC, SLOVAKIA, AND HUNGARY

When World War II ended in 1945, many countries in Eastern Europe came under the control of the Soviet Union. When the Soviet Union broke apart in 1991, the people in Poland, Czechoslovakia, and Hungary once again took charge of their own governments. In 1993, Czechoslovakia split into two independent countries, the Czech Republic and Slovakia.

LEARN ABOUT POLAND, CZECH REPUBLC, SLOVAKIA, AND HUNGARY AS YOU LOOK FOR THESE FUN ITEMS:

- ❏ Barn
- ❏ Bear
- ❏ Bird
- ❏ Bison
- ❏ Butterflies (4)
- ❏ Carrot
- ❏ Cooks (3)
- ❏ Flower
- ❏ Hockey player
- ❏ Music notes

- ❏ Pigs (2)
- ❏ Radio tower
- ❏ Sausage
- ❏ Scarecrows (5)
- ❏ Sheep
- ❏ Tennis ball
- ❏ Tourists
- ❏ Truck
- ❏ Windmill
- ❏ Woolly mammoth

THE NORTHEASTERN REGION IS DENSE WITH TALL TREES AND LAKES.

BUG RIVER

EUROPEAN BISON

PALACE OF CULTURE

OJCOW NATIONAL PARK IN THE SOUTH HAS 50 CAVES WHERE PREHISTORIC PEOPLE LIVED.

REMAINS OF PREHISTORIC MAMMOTHS HAVE ALSO BEEN FOUND THERE.

OUR POPULATION IS 5,400,000 AND OUR LANGUAGES ARE SLOVAK AND HUNGARIAN.

GOULASH, A TRADITIONAL HUNGARIAN DISH, IS A STEW OF MEAT, POTATOES, ONIONS, AND PAPRIKA (A SPICE MADE FROM SWEET RED PEPPERS), AND IS MY FAVORITE DISH TO MAKE.

WE'RE NOT LOST!

BECAUSE MOST OF OUR LAND IS FERTILE, HUNGARIANS PRODUCE ENOUGH FOOD TO FEED THE COUNTRY AND SELL ABROAD.

OUR POPULATION IS 10,100,000.

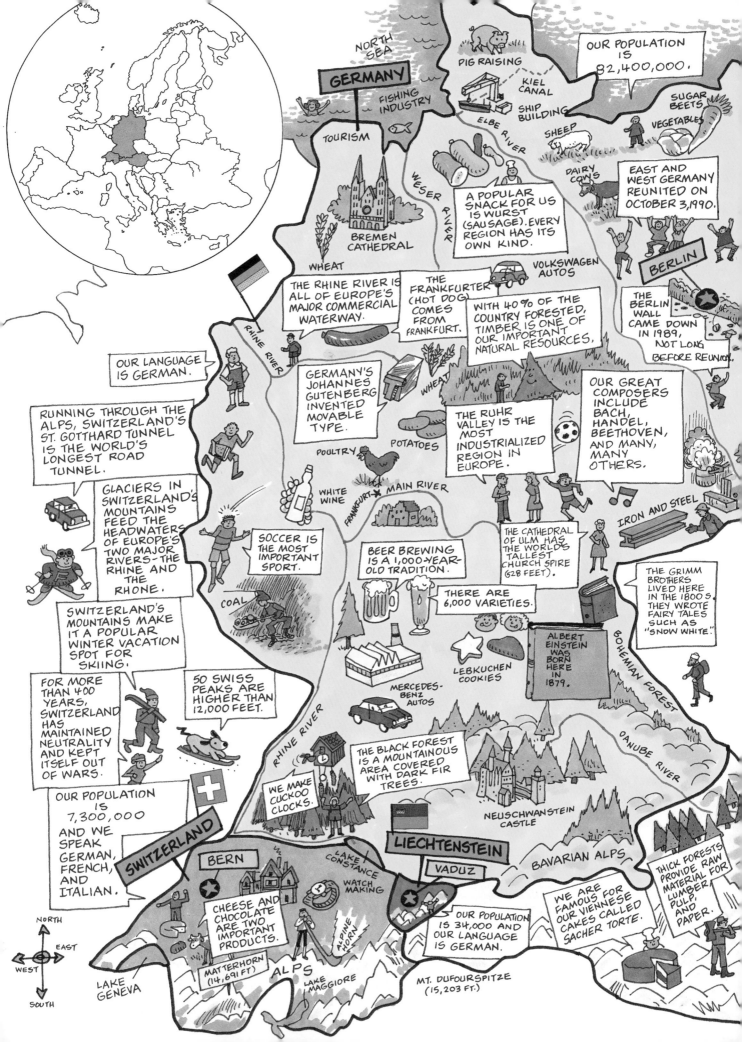

GERMANY, SWITZERLAND, LIECHTENSTEIN, AND AUSTRIA

The countries of Germany, Switzerland, Liechtenstein, and Austria lie in an area some-times known as central Europe. From north to south, this region's landscape changes from marshy plains to snowcapped moutains. It is crossed by two of Europe's longest rivers—the Rhine and the Danube—and by the Alps, the famous mountain range that is the longest and highest mountain range in western Europe.

LEARN ABOUT GERMANY, SWITZERLAND, LIECHTENSTEIN, AND AUSTRIA AS YOU LOOK FOR THESE FUN ITEMS:

- ❏ Alpine horn blower
- ❏ Automobiles (3)
- ❏ Axe
- ❏ Berlin Wall
- ❏ Books (3)
- ❏ Cake
- ❏ Carrot
- ❏ Chicken
- ❏ Coal miner
- ❏ Cookies
- ❏ Cows (2)
- ❏ Cuckoo clock
- ❏ Dogs (2)
- ❏ Great white heron
- ❏ Horse
- ❏ Hot dogs
- ❏ Pigs (2)
- ❏ Soccer ball
- ❏ Telescope
- ❏ Tuba
- ❏ Watch

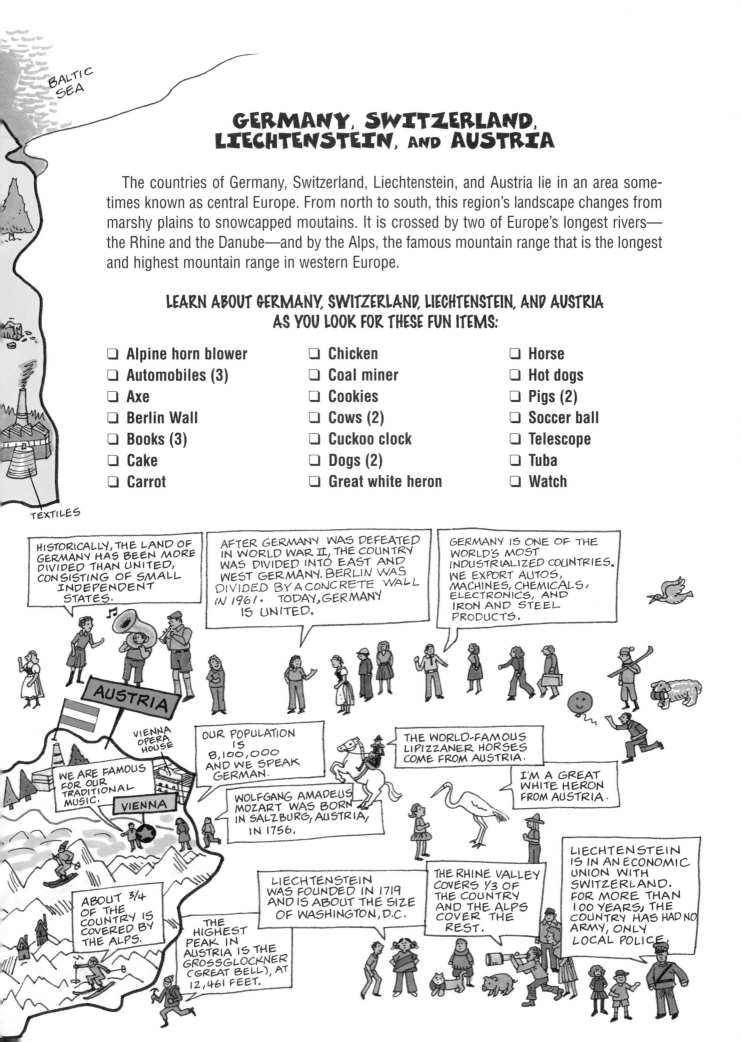

BALTIC SEA

TEXTILES

HISTORICALLY, THE LAND OF GERMANY HAS BEEN MORE DIVIDED THAN UNITED, CONSISTING OF SMALL INDEPENDENT STATES.

AFTER GERMANY WAS DEFEATED IN WORLD WAR II, THE COUNTRY WAS DIVIDED INTO EAST AND WEST GERMANY. BERLIN WAS DIVIDED BY A CONCRETE WALL IN 1961. TODAY, GERMANY IS UNITED.

GERMANY IS ONE OF THE WORLD'S MOST INDUSTRIALIZED COUNTRIES. WE EXPORT AUTOS, MACHINES, CHEMICALS, ELECTRONICS, AND IRON AND STEEL PRODUCTS.

AUSTRIA

VIENNA OPERA HOUSE

WE ARE FAMOUS FOR OUR TRADITIONAL MUSIC.

VIENNA

OUR POPULATION IS 8,100,000 AND WE SPEAK GERMAN.

WOLFGANG AMADEUS MOZART WAS BORN IN SALZBURG, AUSTRIA, IN 1756.

THE WORLD-FAMOUS LIPIZZANER HORSES COME FROM AUSTRIA.

I'M A GREAT WHITE HERON FROM AUSTRIA.

ABOUT 3/4 OF THE COUNTRY IS COVERED BY THE ALPS.

THE HIGHEST PEAK IN AUSTRIA IS THE GROSSGLOCKNER (GREAT BELL), AT 12,461 FEET.

LIECHTENSTEIN WAS FOUNDED IN 1719 AND IS ABOUT THE SIZE OF WASHINGTON, D.C.

THE RHINE VALLEY COVERS 1/3 OF THE COUNTRY AND THE ALPS COVER THE REST.

LIECHTENSTEIN IS IN AN ECONOMIC UNION WITH SWITZERLAND. FOR MORE THAN 100 YEARS, THE COUNTRY HAS HAD NO ARMY, ONLY LOCAL POLICE.

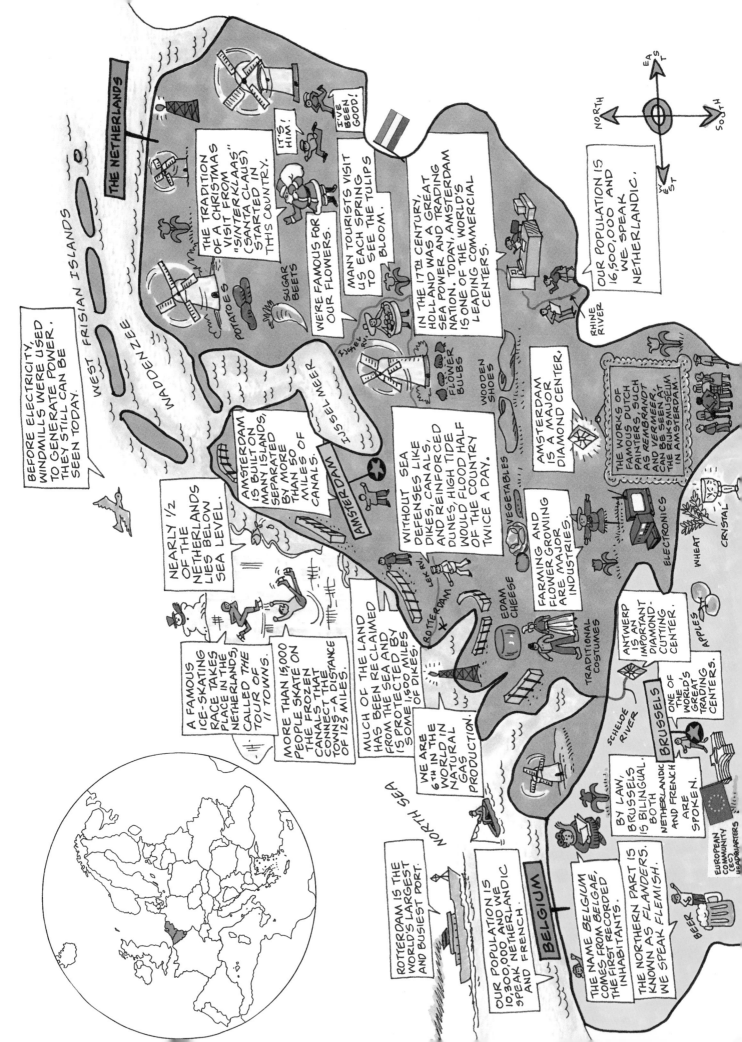

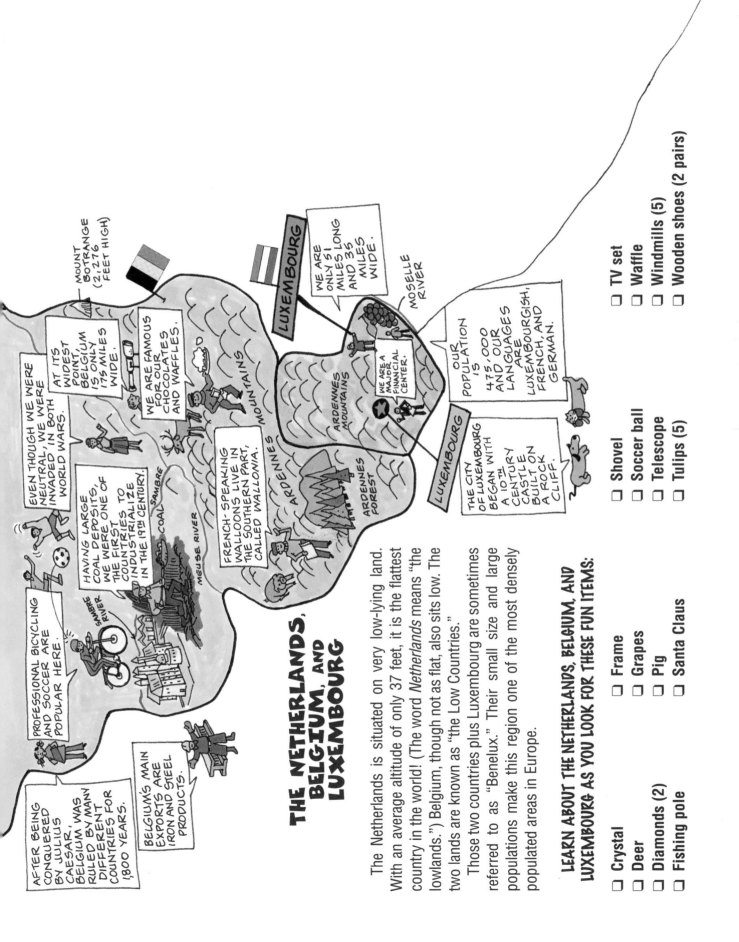

THE NETHERLANDS, BELGIUM, AND LUXEMBOURG

The Netherlands is situated on very low-lying land. With an average altitude of only 37 feet, it is the flattest country in the world! (The word *Netherlands* means "the lowlands.") Belgium, though not as flat, also sits low. The two lands are known as "the Low Countries."

Those two countries plus Luxembourg are sometimes referred to as "Benelux." Their small size and large populations make this region one of the most densely populated areas in Europe.

LEARN ABOUT THE NETHERLANDS, BELGIUM, AND LUXEMBOURG AS YOU LOOK FOR THESE FUN ITEMS:

- ☐ Crystal
- ☐ Deer
- ☐ Diamonds (2)
- ☐ Fishing pole
- ☐ Frame
- ☐ Grapes
- ☐ Pig
- ☐ Santa Claus
- ☐ Shovel
- ☐ Soccer ball
- ☐ Telescope
- ☐ Tulips (5)
- ☐ TV set
- ☐ Waffle
- ☐ Windmills (5)
- ☐ Wooden shoes (2 pairs)

FRANCE AND MONACO

France is one of the oldest countries in Europe. It also is one of the world's leading countries in terms of culture, historic and political influence, industry, and agriculture. The capital and cultural center is the city of Paris, nicknamed "the City of Light."

At France's southeastern corner lies Monaco, one of the world's smallest nations. (*Monaco* is also the name of its capital city.)

LEARN ABOUT FRANCE AND MONACO AS YOU LOOK FOR THESE FUN ITEMS:

- ❏ **Apples (2)**
- ❏ **Artichoke**
- ❏ **Artist**
- ❏ **Automobile**
- ❏ **Chef**
- ❏ **Cyclist**
- ❏ **Dice**
- ❏ **Eels**
- ❏ **Eiffel Tower**
- ❏ **Geese (2)**
- ❏ **Mouse**
- ❏ **Musician**
- ❏ **Mustard**
- ❏ **Napoleon**
- ❏ **Paper airplane**
- ❏ **Perfume bottle**
- ❏ **Pig**
- ❏ **Red balloon**
- ❏ **Skier**
- ❏ **Snail**
- ❏ **Soccer ball**
- ❏ **Umbrellas (2)**
- ❏ **Walnuts**

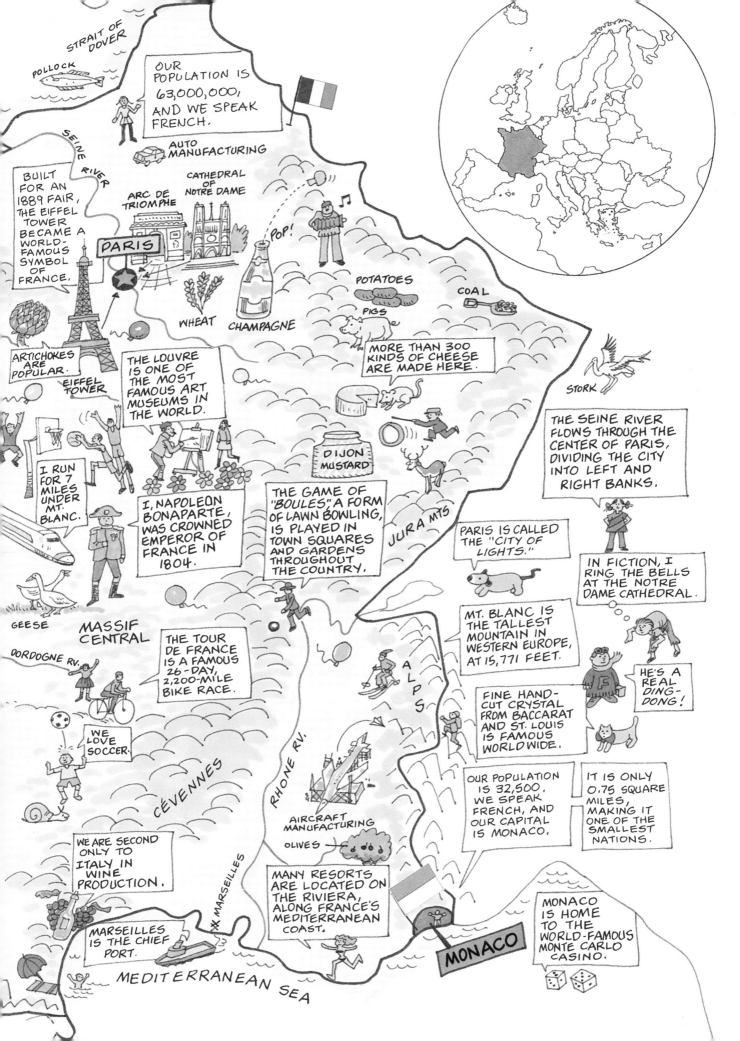

THE IBERIAN PENINSULA

Spain, Portugal, and Andorra share a piece of land called the Iberian Peninsula. (A *peninsula* is a land area with water on all sides except for a neck of land connected to a larger landmass.) Spain and Portugal have long seafaring histories. Their explorers and settlers once ruled empires in Africa, Asia, North America, and South America. Tiny Andorra, tucked into an area of the Pyrenees Mountains, is landlocked.

Today, fishing, farming, and tourism are major industries in Spain and Portugal. More than 60 million tourists each year visit their historical cities and sun-drenched beaches.

LEARN ABOUT THE IBERIAN PENINSULA AS YOU LOOK FOR THESE FUN ITEMS:

- ☐ **Anchovies**
- ☐ **Bottles (5)**
- ☐ **Brown bear**
- ☐ **Bulls (3)**
- ☐ **Cheese**
- ☐ **Cork**
- ☐ **Guitar**
- ☐ **Ibex**
- ☐ **Olive tree**
- ☐ **Skier**
- ☐ **Sunflowers (4)**
- ☐ **Umbrellas (3)**
- ☐ **Windmill**
- ☐ **Windsurfers (3)**

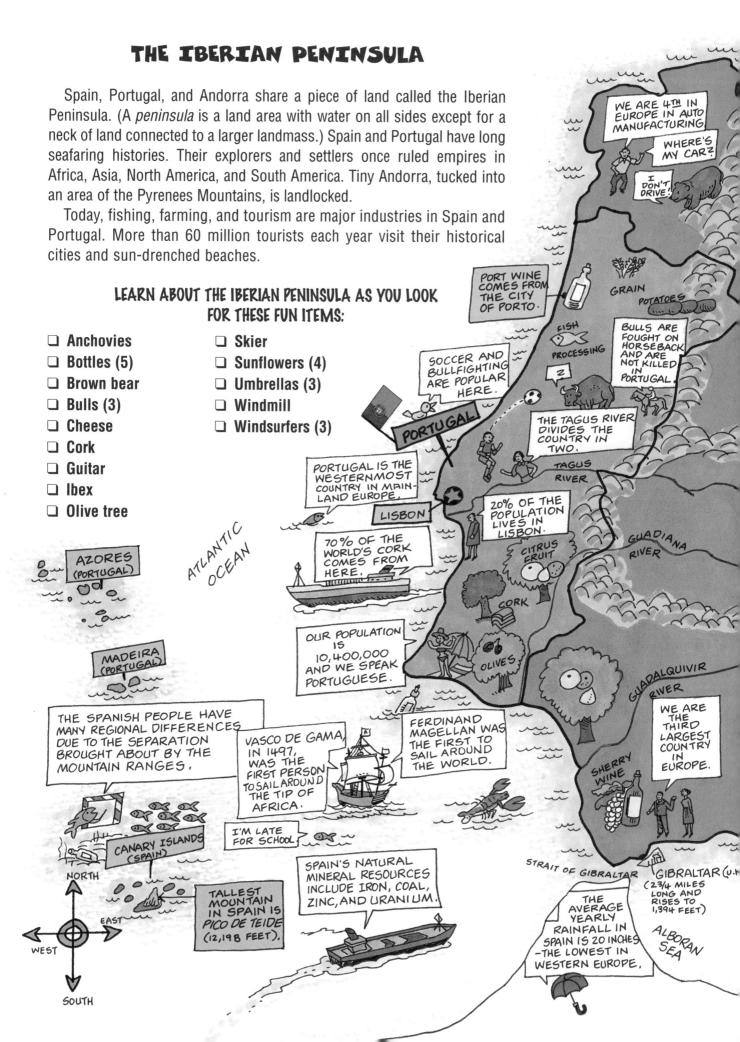

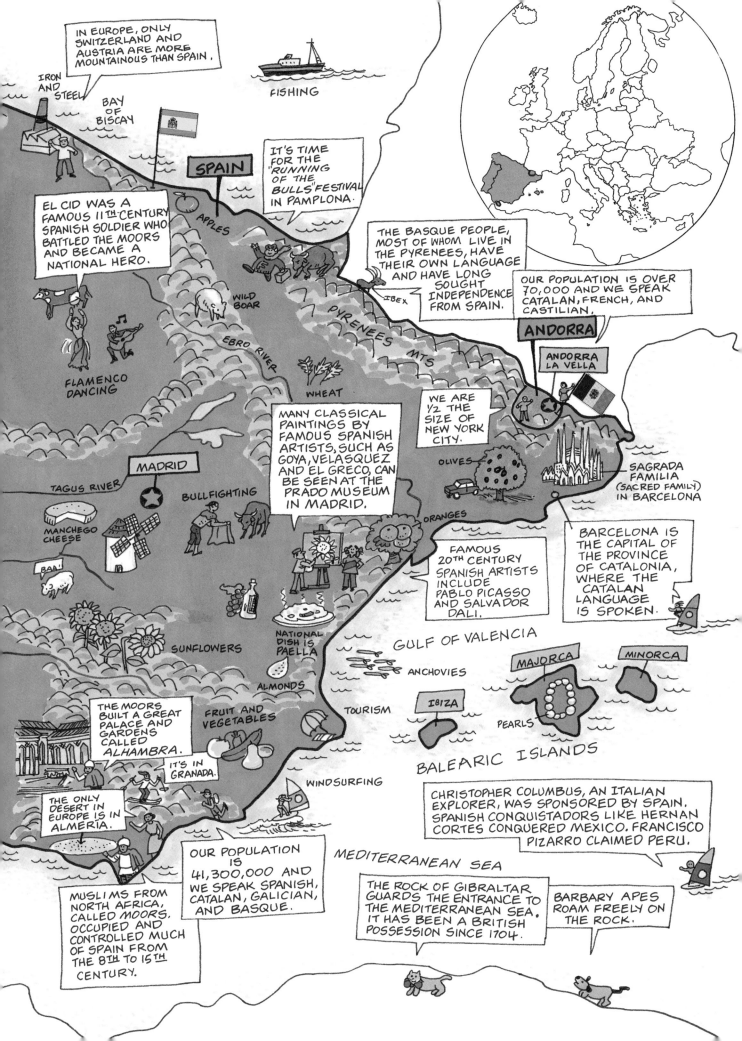

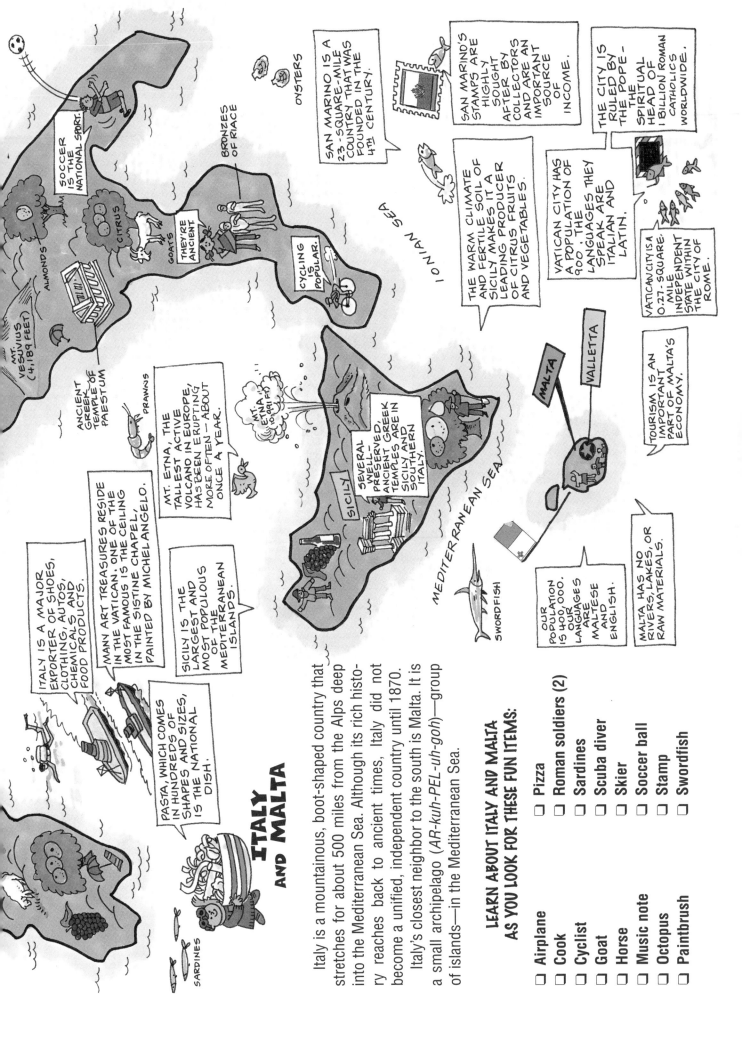

ITALY and MALTA

Italy is a mountainous, boot-shaped country that stretches for about 500 miles deep into the Mediterranean Sea. Although its rich history reaches back to ancient times, Italy did not become a unified, independent country until 1870.

Italy's closest neighbor to the south is Malta. It is a small archipelago (AR-kuh-PEL-uh-goh)—group of islands—in the Mediterranean Sea.

LEARN ABOUT ITALY AND MALTA AS YOU LOOK FOR THESE FUN ITEMS:

☐ Airplane
☐ Cook
☐ Cyclist
☐ Goat
☐ Horse
☐ Music note
☐ Octopus
☐ Paintbrush

☐ Pizza
☐ Roman soldiers (2)
☐ Sardines
☐ Scuba diver
☐ Skier
☐ Soccer ball
☐ Stamp
☐ Swordfish

SOCCER IS THE NATIONAL SPORT.

CITRUS

GOATS

THEY'RE ANCIENT.

BRONZES OF RIACE

CYCLING IS POPULAR.

ALMONDS

MT. VESUVIUS (4,189 FEET)

ANCIENT GREEK TEMPLE OF PAESTUM

PRAWNS

OYSTERS

SAN MARINO IS A 23-SQUARE-MILE COUNTRY THAT WAS FOUNDED IN THE 4TH CENTURY.

SAN MARINO'S STAMPS ARE HIGHLY SOUGHT AFTER BY COLLECTORS AND ARE AN IMPORTANT SOURCE OF INCOME.

THE CITY IS RULED BY THE POPE—THE SPIRITUAL HEAD OF 1 BILLION ROMAN CATHOLICS WORLDWIDE.

THE WARM CLIMATE AND FERTILE SOIL OF SICILY MAKES IT A LEADING PRODUCER OF CITRUS FRUITS AND VEGETABLES.

VATICAN CITY HAS A POPULATION OF 900. THE LANGUAGES THEY SPEAK ARE ITALIAN AND LATIN.

VATICAN CITY IS A 0.27-SQUARE-MILE INDEPENDENT STATE WITHIN THE CITY OF ROME.

IONIAN SEA

MT. ETNA, THE TALLEST ACTIVE VOLCANO IN EUROPE, HAS BEEN ERUPTING MORE OFTEN—ABOUT ONCE A YEAR.

MT. ETNA (10,991 FT.)

SEVERAL WELL-PRESERVED, ANCIENT GREEK TEMPLES ARE IN SICILY AND SOUTHERN ITALY.

SICILY

MALTA

VALLETTA

TOURISM IS AN IMPORTANT PART OF MALTA'S ECONOMY.

MEDITERRANEAN SEA

SWORDFISH

OUR POPULATION IS 400,000. OUR LANGUAGES ARE MALTESE AND ENGLISH.

MALTA HAS NO RIVERS, LAKES, OR RAW MATERIALS.

ITALY IS A MAJOR EXPORTER OF SHOES, CLOTHING, AUTOS, CHEMICALS, AND FOOD PRODUCTS.

MANY ART TREASURES RESIDE IN THE VATICAN. ONE OF THE MOST FAMOUS IS THE CEILING IN THE SISTINE CHAPEL, PAINTED BY MICHELANGELO.

PASTA, WHICH COMES IN HUNDREDS OF SHAPES AND SIZES, IS THE NATIONAL DISH.

SICILY IS THE LARGEST AND MOST POPULOUS OF THE MEDITERRANEAN ISLANDS.

SARDINES

THE BALKAN NATIONS

Much of this part of eastern Europe, known as the Balkans, was ruled by Turkey from the end of the 15th century until 1913. (The name *Balkan* comes from the Balkan Mountains of Bulgaria.) After World War I, several regions were combined to form Yugoslavia. It was heavily influenced by its huge neighbor, the Soviet Union. Soon after the Soviet Union broke apart in 1991, so did Yugoslavia. That land is now five independent countries: Serbia and Montenegro, Slovenia, Croatia, Bosnia and Herzegovina, and Macedonia.

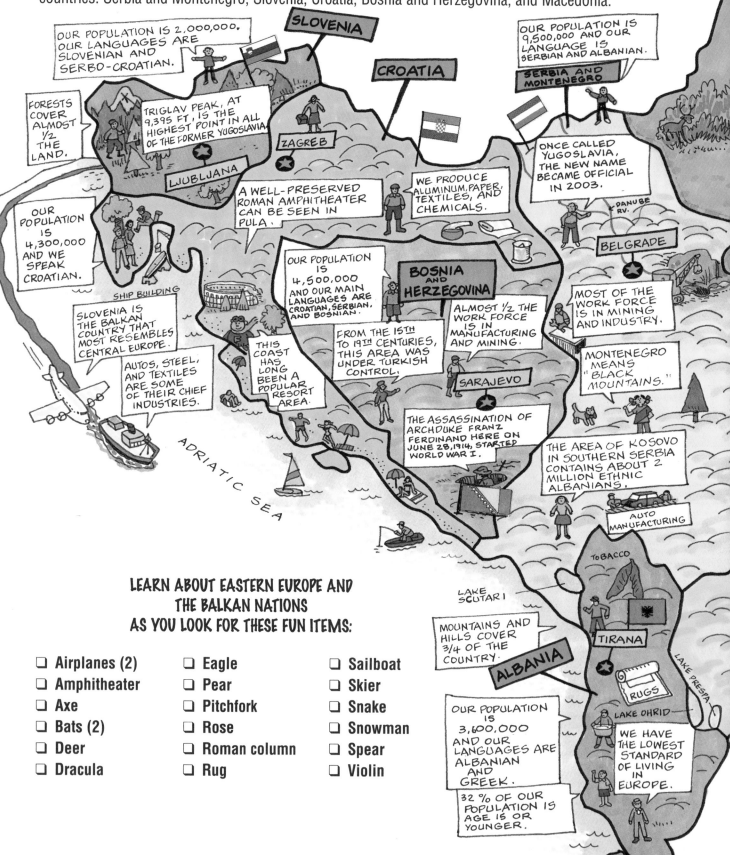

OUR POPULATION IS 2,000,000. OUR LANGUAGES ARE SLOVENIAN AND SERBO-CROATIAN.

SLOVENIA

OUR POPULATION IS 9,500,000 AND OUR LANGUAGE IS SERBIAN AND ALBANIAN.

FORESTS COVER ALMOST ½ THE LAND.

TRIGLAV PEAK, AT 9,395 FT, IS THE HIGHEST POINT IN ALL OF THE FORMER YUGOSLAVIA.

CROATIA

SERBIA AND MONTENEGRO

ZAGREB

ONCE CALLED YUGOSLAVIA, THE NEW NAME BECAME OFFICIAL IN 2003.

LJUBLJANA

A WELL-PRESERVED ROMAN AMPHITHEATER CAN BE SEEN IN PULA.

WE PRODUCE ALUMINUM, PAPER, TEXTILES, AND CHEMICALS.

DANUBE RV.

OUR POPULATION IS 4,300,000 AND WE SPEAK CROATIAN.

BELGRADE

SHIP BUILDING

OUR POPULATION IS 4,500,000 AND OUR MAIN LANGUAGES ARE CROATIAN, SERBIAN, AND BOSNIAN.

BOSNIA AND HERZEGOVINA

MOST OF THE WORK FORCE IS IN MINING AND INDUSTRY.

SLOVENIA IS THE BALKAN COUNTRY THAT MOST RESEMBLES CENTRAL EUROPE.

THIS COAST HAS LONG BEEN A POPULAR RESORT AREA.

FROM THE 15TH TO 19TH CENTURIES, THIS AREA WAS UNDER TURKISH CONTROL.

ALMOST ½ THE WORK FORCE IS IN MANUFACTURING AND MINING.

MONTENEGRO MEANS "BLACK MOUNTAINS."

AUTOS, STEEL, AND TEXTILES ARE SOME OF THEIR CHIEF INDUSTRIES.

SARAJEVO

THE ASSASSINATION OF ARCHDUKE FRANZ FERDINAND HERE ON JUNE 28, 1914, STARTED WORLD WAR I.

THE AREA OF KOSOVO IN SOUTHERN SERBIA CONTAINS ABOUT 2 MILLION ETHNIC ALBANIANS.

ADRIATIC SEA

AUTO MANUFACTURING

TOBACCO

LAKE SCUTARI

LEARN ABOUT EASTERN EUROPE AND THE BALKAN NATIONS AS YOU LOOK FOR THESE FUN ITEMS:

MOUNTAINS AND HILLS COVER 3/4 OF THE COUNTRY.

TIRANA

ALBANIA

LAKE PRESPA

RUGS

- ☐ Airplanes (2)
- ☐ Amphitheater
- ☐ Axe
- ☐ Bats (2)
- ☐ Deer
- ☐ Dracula
- ☐ Eagle
- ☐ Pear
- ☐ Pitchfork
- ☐ Rose
- ☐ Roman column
- ☐ Rug
- ☐ Sailboat
- ☐ Skier
- ☐ Snake
- ☐ Snowman
- ☐ Spear
- ☐ Violin

LAKE OHRID

OUR POPULATION IS 3,600,000 AND OUR LANGUAGES ARE ALBANIAN AND GREEK.

WE HAVE THE LOWEST STANDARD OF LIVING IN EUROPE.

32% OF OUR POPULATION IS AGE 15 OR YOUNGER.

GREECE

The ideals of Western democracy were born in Greece about 2,500 years ago. The art, philosophy, theater, mythology, science, and architecture that flourished there formed the basis of Western civilization.

LEARN ABOUT GREECE AS YOU LOOK FOR THESE FUN ITEMS:
- ☐ Book
- ☐ Cotton
- ☐ Grapes
- ☐ Octopus
- ☐ Olympic torch bearer
- ☐ Sailboat
- ☐ Stone lion
- ☐ Telescope

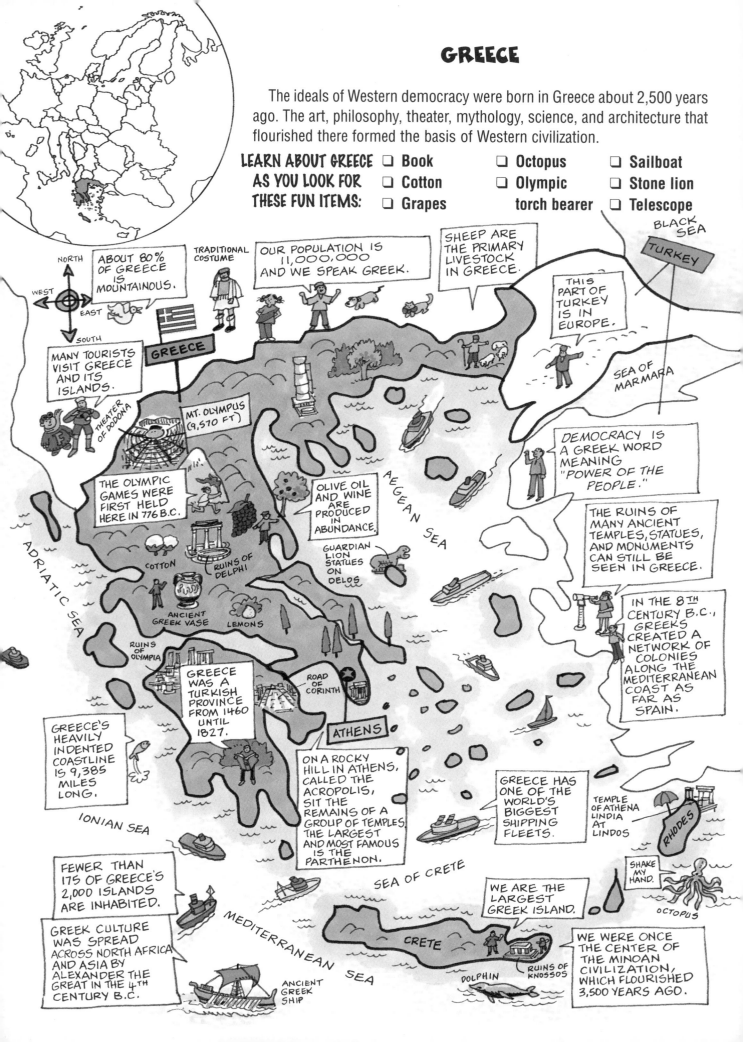

NORTH
WEST
EAST
SOUTH

BLACK SEA

TURKEY

TRADITIONAL COSTUME

ABOUT 80% OF GREECE IS MOUNTAINOUS.

OUR POPULATION IS 11,000,000 AND WE SPEAK GREEK.

SHEEP ARE THE PRIMARY LIVESTOCK IN GREECE.

THIS PART OF TURKEY IS IN EUROPE.

GREECE

MANY TOURISTS VISIT GREECE AND ITS ISLANDS.

THEATER OF DODONA

MT. OLYMPUS (9,570 FT)

SEA OF MARMARA

DEMOCRACY IS A GREEK WORD MEANING "POWER OF THE PEOPLE."

THE OLYMPIC GAMES WERE FIRST HELD HERE IN 776 B.C.

OLIVE OIL AND WINE ARE PRODUCED IN ABUNDANCE.

AEGEAN SEA

THE RUINS OF MANY ANCIENT TEMPLES, STATUES, AND MONUMENTS CAN STILL BE SEEN IN GREECE.

COTTON

RUINS OF DELPHI

GUARDIAN LION STATUES ON DELOS

IN THE 8TH CENTURY B.C., GREEKS CREATED A NETWORK OF COLONIES ALONG THE MEDITERRANEAN COAST AS FAR AS SPAIN.

ADRIATIC SEA

ANCIENT GREEK VASE

LEMONS

RUINS OF OLYMPIA

GREECE WAS A TURKISH PROVINCE FROM 1460 UNTIL 1827.

ROAD OF CORINTH

GREECE'S HEAVILY INDENTED COASTLINE IS 9,385 MILES LONG.

ATHENS

ON A ROCKY HILL IN ATHENS, CALLED THE ACROPOLIS, SIT THE REMAINS OF A GROUP OF TEMPLES. THE LARGEST AND MOST FAMOUS IS THE PARTHENON.

GREECE HAS ONE OF THE WORLD'S BIGGEST SHIPPING FLEETS.

TEMPLE OF ATHENA LINDIA AT LINDOS

RHODES

SHAKE MY HAND.

IONIAN SEA

FEWER THAN 175 OF GREECE'S 2,000 ISLANDS ARE INHABITED.

SEA OF CRETE

WE ARE THE LARGEST GREEK ISLAND.

OCTOPUS

GREEK CULTURE WAS SPREAD ACROSS NORTH AFRICA AND ASIA BY ALEXANDER THE GREAT IN THE 4TH CENTURY B.C.

MEDITERRANEAN SEA

CRETE

ANCIENT GREEK SHIP

DOLPHIN

RUINS OF KNOSSOS

WE WERE ONCE THE CENTER OF THE MINOAN CIVILIZATION, WHICH FLOURISHED 3,500 YEARS AGO.

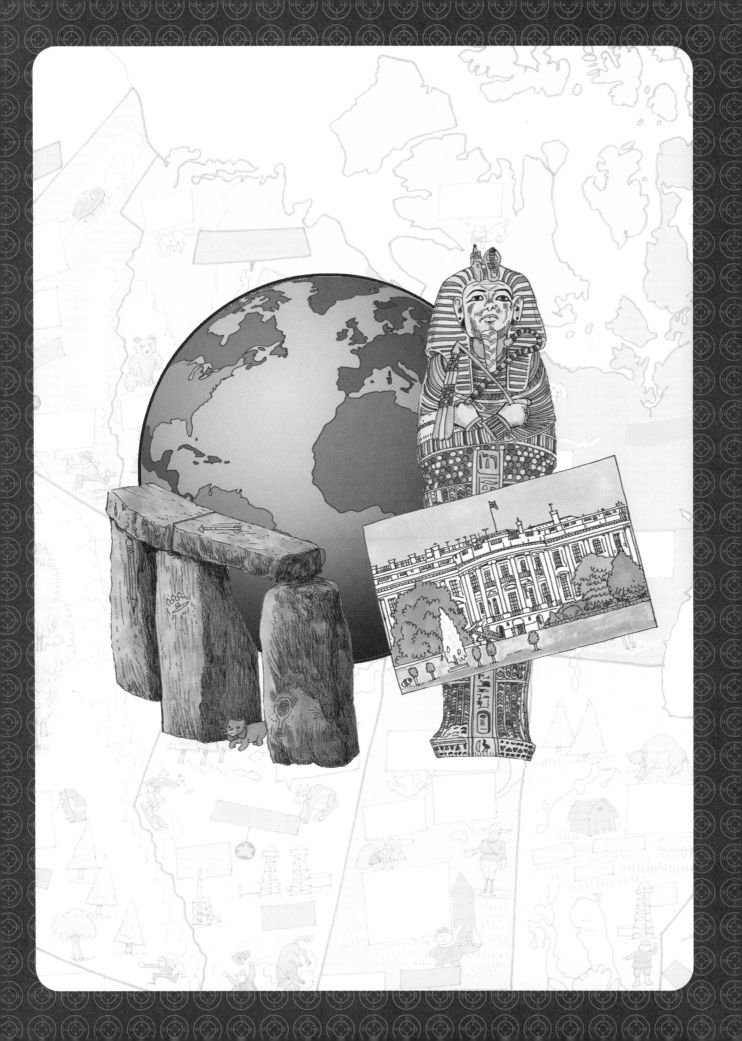

LOOK
& LOOK AGAIN
DINOSAURS

FAST-FOODASAURUS

FIND THESE ITEMS:

- ☐ Banana peel
- ☐ Bell
- ☐ Beret
- ☐ Bones (2)
- ☐ Book
- ☐ Bow tie
- ☐ Broken balloon
- ☐ Cactus
- ☐ Candle
- ☐ Chef
- ☐ Crayon
- ☐ Envelope
- ☐ Eyeglasses
- ☐ Fish (2)
- ☐ Flower
- ☐ Flying bat
- ☐ Football
- ☐ Heart
- ☐ Key
- ☐ Lost sock
- ☐ Mouse hole
- ☐ Mushroom
- ☐ Music note
- ☐ Net
- ☐ Rabbit
- ☐ Saw
- ☐ Scarf
- ☐ Star
- ☐ Sunglasses
- ☐ Tattoo
- ☐ Toothbrush
- ☐ Umbrella
- ☐ Whistle

FAMILY REUNION PORTRAITASAURUS

FIND THESE ITEMS:

- ☐ Baseball
- ☐ Baseball bat
- ☐ Baseball caps (2)
- ☐ Cactus
- ☐ Candle
- ☐ Coffee cup
- ☐ Coffeepot
- ☐ Cookie
- ☐ Dino ordering pizza
- ☐ Egg
- ☐ Eyeglasses
- ☐ Football
- ☐ Fish
- ☐ Flower
- ☐ Heart
- ☐ Horseshoe
- ☐ Mouse
- ☐ Moustache
- ☐ Paintbrush
- ☐ Pear
- ☐ Ring
- ☐ Rollerskate
- ☐ Sleeping dino
- ☐ Stars (2)
- ☐ Straw
- ☐ Yo-yo

SKI-A-SAURUS MOUNTAIN

FIND ALL THE LETTERS
OF THE ALPHABET:

- ☐ A
- ☐ B
- ☐ C
- ☐ D
- ☐ E
- ☐ F
- ☐ G
- ☐ H
- ☐ I
- ☐ J
- ☐ K
- ☐ L
- ☐ M
- ☐ N
- ☐ O
- ☐ P
- ☐ Q
- ☐ R
- ☐ S
- ☐ T
- ☐ U
- ☐ V
- ☐ W
- ☐ X
- ☐ Y
- ☐ Z
- ☐ Baseball hat
- ☐ Flower
- ☐ Heart
- ☐ Pizza delivery dino
- ☐ Star

THE PARTY-A-SAURUS CLUB

FIND THESE ITEMS:

- ☐ Apple
- ☐ Banana peel
- ☐ Barber pole
- ☐ Baseball bat
- ☐ Birdcage
- ☐ Cactus
- ☐ Capless dino
- ☐ Cupcake
- ☐ Fire hydrant
- ☐ Fish
- ☐ Flower
- ☐ Ghost
- ☐ Golf club
- ☐ Ice-cream cone
- ☐ Kite
- ☐ Mailbox
- ☐ Mouse hole
- ☐ Mustaches (2)
- ☐ Paintbrush
- ☐ Pencil
- ☐ Quarter moon
- ☐ Rabbit
- ☐ Ring
- ☐ Scarf
- ☐ Seal
- ☐ Star
- ☐ Tepee
- ☐ Thermometer
- ☐ Watermelon slice
- ☐ Whale

SHOP-A-HOLIC SAURUS

FIND THESE ITEMS:

- ☐ Arrows (5)
- ☐ Books (2)
- ☐ Bird
- ☐ Broken bulb
- ☐ Bubble gum bubble
- ☐ Cane
- ☐ Cap
- ☐ Coffee cup
- ☐ Earmuffs
- ☐ Fish
- ☐ Football
- ☐ Lost balloon
- ☐ Lost sock
- ☐ Mailbox
- ☐ Music note
- ☐ Newspaper reader
- ☐ Pencil
- ☐ Phonograph
- ☐ Rocking chair
- ☐ Scarves (2)
- ☐ Shoulder bag
- ☐ Star
- ☐ Tires (4)
- ☐ Trash cans (2)
- ☐ Umbrella
- ☐ Vacant store
- ☐ Volcano
- ☐ Water fountain

MT. VOLCANOSAURUS

FIND THESE ITEMS:

- [ ] Automobile
- [ ] Banana
- [ ] Bath brush
- [ ] Beachball
- [ ] Boot
- [ ] Carrot
- [ ] Clothespin
- [ ] Cow
- [ ] Cowboy hat
- [ ] Crayon
- [ ] Daisy
- [ ] Dart
- [ ] Fish
- [ ] Flying bat
- [ ] Football
- [ ] Ghost
- [ ] Hockey stick
- [ ] Humpty Dumpty
- [ ] Keys (2)
- [ ] Kite
- [ ] Lightbulb
- [ ] Mitten
- [ ] Octopus
- [ ] Pumpkins (2)
- [ ] Rabbit
- [ ] Rooster
- [ ] Sand pail
- [ ] Sock
- [ ] Telescope
- [ ] Television
- [ ] Umbrella

HOLLYWOOD-A-SAURUS

FIND THESE ITEMS:

- [ ] Arrows (2)
- [ ] Baseball cap
- [ ] Beret
- [ ] Bones (2)
- [ ] Bouquet of flowers
- [ ] Burned-out bulb
- [ ] Dino ordering pizza
- [ ] Escaped balloon
- [ ] Feather
- [ ] Football
- [ ] Ice-cream cone
- [ ] Hammer
- [ ] Heart
- [ ] Hot dog
- [ ] Lost shoe
- [ ] Microphone
- [ ] Moustache
- [ ] Pearl necklace
- [ ] Pencil
- [ ] Pizza
- [ ] Scissors
- [ ] Screwdriver
- [ ] Stars (2)
- [ ] Sunglasses (2)
- [ ] Telescope
- [ ] Yo-yo

AIRPORT-A-SAURUS

FIND THESE ITEMS:

- ☐ Accordion
- ☐ Arrow
- ☐ Book
- ☐ Bow tie
- ☐ Candy cane
- ☐ Crown
- ☐ Eyeglasses
- ☐ Flying carpet
- ☐ Flying elephant
- ☐ Flying fish
- ☐ Flying saucer
- ☐ Football
- ☐ Hat box
- ☐ Heart
- ☐ Hot-air balloon
- ☐ Hot dog
- ☐ Ice-cream pop
- ☐ Kite
- ☐ Paper airplane
- ☐ Periscope
- ☐ Pizza box
- ☐ Propellers (2)
- ☐ Roller skates
- ☐ Sailor cap
- ☐ Star
- ☐ Straw
- ☐ Top hat
- ☐ Umbrella
- ☐ Watering can
- ☐ Yo-yo's (2)

SENIOR-CITIZENSAURUS

FIND THESE ITEMS:

- ☐ Anchor
- ☐ Apple
- ☐ Balloon
- ☐ Balls (2)
- ☐ Banana
- ☐ Bow tie
- ☐ Canes (2)
- ☐ Coffeepot
- ☐ Coonskin cap
- ☐ Crown
- ☐ Cup
- ☐ Drum
- ☐ Eyeglasses (4)
- ☐ Feather
- ☐ High-heeled shoes
- ☐ Kite
- ☐ Moustache
- ☐ Neckties (3)
- ☐ Paddle
- ☐ Paintbrush
- ☐ Pencil
- ☐ Pocketbook
- ☐ Propeller
- ☐ Ring
- ☐ Sailboat
- ☐ Sailor cap
- ☐ Skateboard
- ☐ Sunglasses
- ☐ Top hat
- ☐ Turtle
- ☐ Yo-yo

CYBER-SAURUS

FIND THESE ITEMS:

- ☐ Apple core
- ☐ Baseball
- ☐ Baseball bat
- ☐ Cactus
- ☐ Drum
- ☐ Elephant
- ☐ Eyeglasses
- ☐ Fish
- ☐ Flower
- ☐ Ghost
- ☐ Hamburger
- ☐ Hearts (3)
- ☐ Horse
- ☐ Igloo
- ☐ Jester
- ☐ Knitting needle
- ☐ Laundry
- ☐ Lion
- ☐ Mouse
- ☐ Moustache
- ☐ Net
- ☐ Oil can
- ☐ Pencil
- ☐ Penguin
- ☐ Plunger
- ☐ Rabbit

MULTI-CINEMA-SAURUS

FIND THESE ITEMS:

- ☐ "3"
- ☐ Backpack
- ☐ Balloon
- ☐ Bird
- ☐ Bowling bag
- ☐ Burned-out lightbulbs (4)
- ☐ Cane
- ☐ Cell phone
- ☐ Dollar bill
- ☐ Football helmet
- ☐ Gum
- ☐ Hearts (3)
- ☐ Ice-cream pop
- ☐ Lollipop
- ☐ Missing lightbulb
- ☐ Necktie
- ☐ Pillow
- ☐ Rollerskate
- ☐ Scooter
- ☐ Skier
- ☐ Straw
- ☐ Suspenders
- ☐ Toothbrush
- ☐ Top hat
- ☐ Turban
- ☐ Umbrella
- ☐ Volcano

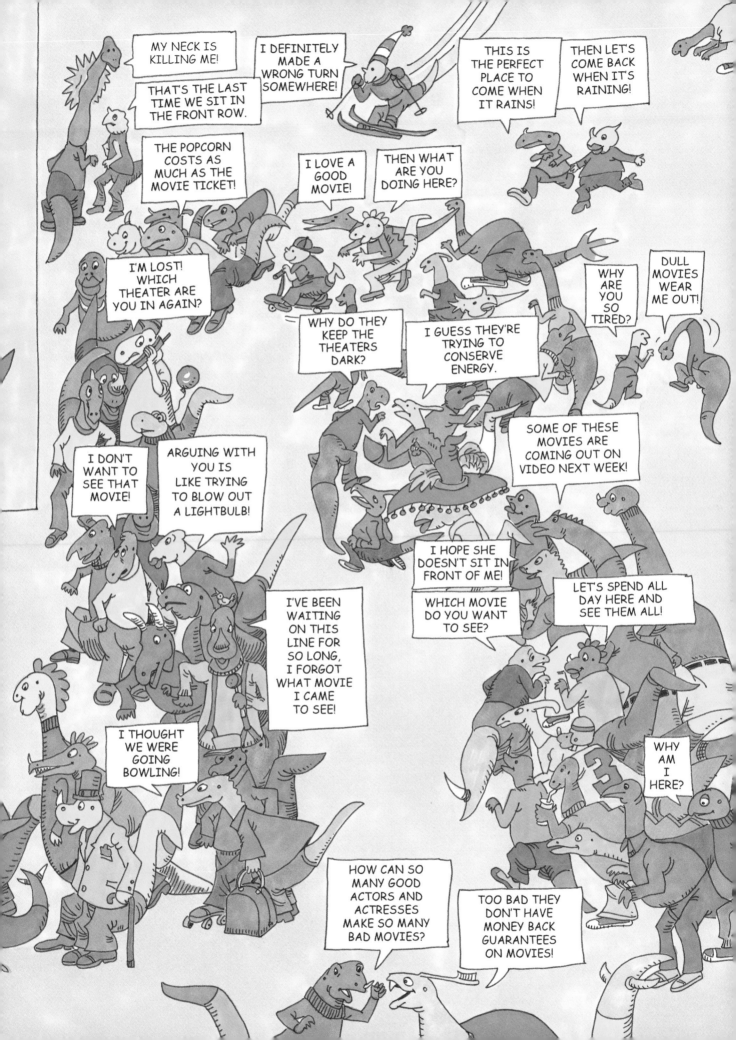

WELCOME TO THE TRIVIA-SAURUS CONVENTION

FIND THESE ITEMS:

- ☐ Astronaut
- ☐ Automobile
- ☐ Banana peel
- ☐ Baseball cap
- ☐ Book
- ☐ Candle
- ☐ Candy cane
- ☐ Cup
- ☐ Eyeglasses
- ☐ Feather
- ☐ Flower
- ☐ Flying bat
- ☐ Ghost
- ☐ Hearts (4)
- ☐ Ice-cream pop
- ☐ Ice skates
- ☐ Jack-o'-lantern
- ☐ Keys (2)
- ☐ Necktie
- ☐ Pencil
- ☐ Pizza delivery dino
- ☐ Pointy beard
- ☐ Propeller
- ☐ Purse
- ☐ Rabbit
- ☐ Rollerskate
- ☐ Scarf
- ☐ Sunglasses
- ☐ Volcano
- ☐ Yo-yo

LUNCH ROOM-A-SAURUS

FIND THESE ITEMS:

- ☐ Alien
- ☐ Backpack
- ☐ Banana peel
- ☐ Bones (2)
- ☐ Broken heart
- ☐ Broom
- ☐ Candle
- ☐ Cell phone
- ☐ Cook
- ☐ Dino ordering pizza
- ☐ Fire hydrant
- ☐ Fish
- ☐ Football helmet
- ☐ Guitar
- ☐ Hammer
- ☐ Ice-cream cone
- ☐ Music note
- ☐ Napkin dispenser
- ☐ Necktie
- ☐ Old tire
- ☐ Paper airplane
- ☐ Pencils (3)
- ☐ Periscope
- ☐ Roller skate
- ☐ Santa cap
- ☐ Skateboard
- ☐ Sock
- ☐ Umbrella
- ☐ Worm

FARM-A-SAURUS

FIND THESE ITEMS:

- ☐ Axe
- ☐ Balloon
- ☐ Candy cane
- ☐ Coffeepot
- ☐ Cow
- ☐ Crayons (3)
- ☐ Crows (7)
- ☐ Dog
- ☐ Duck
- ☐ Empty flowerpot
- ☐ Golf ball
- ☐ Golf club
- ☐ Hoe
- ☐ Horseshoe
- ☐ Ice-cream cone
- ☐ Key
- ☐ Kite
- ☐ Mouse
- ☐ Neckerchief
- ☐ Pear
- ☐ Pencil
- ☐ Pitchfork
- ☐ Rooster
- ☐ Shovel
- ☐ Snake
- ☐ Star
- ☐ Tic-tac-toe
- ☐ Tires (7)
- ☐ Toothbrush
- ☐ Top hat
- ☐ Turtle
- ☐ Watering can
- ☐ Wristwatch

SKATEBOARD-A-SAURUS

FIND THESE ITEMS:

- ☐ Auto
- ☐ Band-aid
- ☐ Banana peel
- ☐ Baseball cap
- ☐ Broken heart
- ☐ Cactus
- ☐ Doghouse
- ☐ Fish (2)
- ☐ Flashlight
- ☐ Ghost
- ☐ Hammer
- ☐ Helmet
- ☐ Lost shoe
- ☐ Motorized board
- ☐ Mushroom
- ☐ Pencil
- ☐ Periscope
- ☐ Pie
- ☐ Pizza
- ☐ Pogo stick
- ☐ Ring
- ☐ Scarf
- ☐ Shark fin
- ☐ Sled
- ☐ Star
- ☐ Three-wheeled board
- ☐ Top hat
- ☐ Turtle
- ☐ Winged board
- ☐ Yo-yo

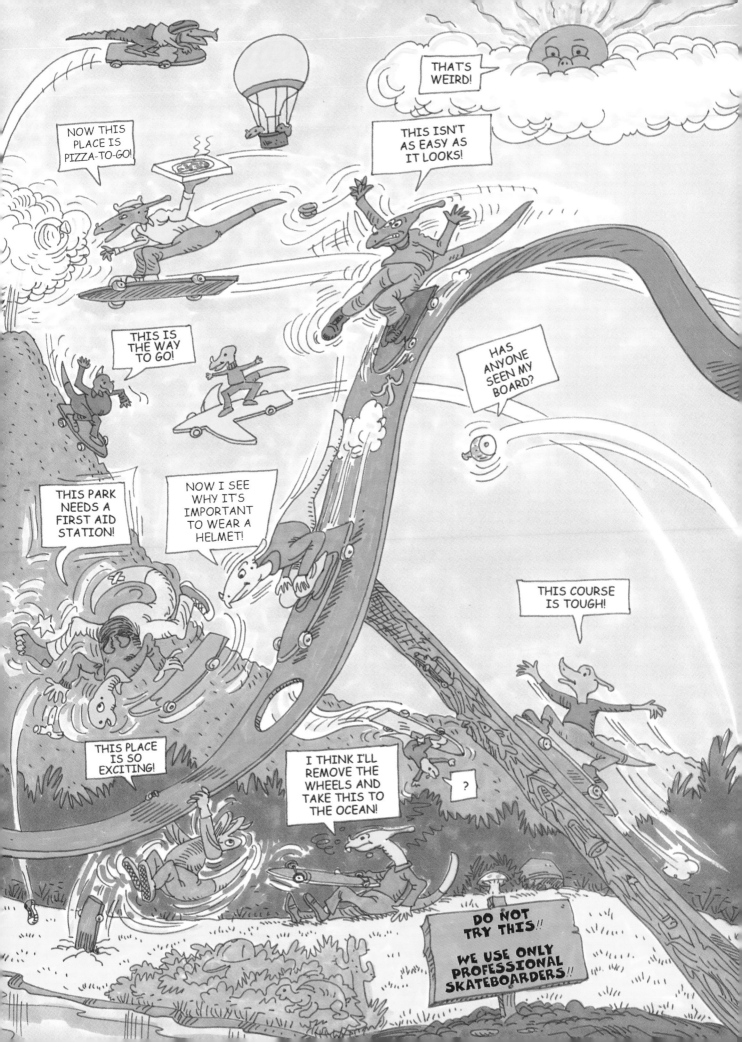

ROBOTIC-A-SAURUS

FIND THESE ITEMS:

- ☐ Arrow
- ☐ Balloon
- ☐ Banana peel
- ☐ Bow tie
- ☐ Brush
- ☐ Crystal ball
- ☐ Fire hydrant
- ☐ Hammer
- ☐ Hearts (2)
- ☐ Ice-cream cone
- ☐ Ice skates
- ☐ Kite
- ☐ Light bulbs (2)
- ☐ Loose screw
- ☐ Necktie
- ☐ Oil can
- ☐ Pencils (2)
- ☐ Pizza
- ☐ Roller skates
- ☐ Satellite dish
- ☐ Shoulder bag
- ☐ Star
- ☐ Sunglasses
- ☐ Telescope
- ☐ Umbrella
- ☐ Vacuum
- ☐ Yo-yo

SO YOU WANT TO BE A
STAR-A-SAURUS

FIND THESE ITEMS:

- [ ] Beret
- [ ] Bird
- [ ] Bottle
- [ ] Bow ties (2)
- [ ] Box
- [ ] Candle
- [ ] Clipboard
- [ ] Crown
- [ ] Dracula-saurus
- [ ] Drum
- [ ] Flower
- [ ] Fork
- [ ] Frying pan
- [ ] Ghost
- [ ] Heart
- [ ] Medal
- [ ] Mustaches (2)
- [ ] Pearl necklace
- [ ] Pencils (2)
- [ ] Periscope
- [ ] Pointy beards (2)
- [ ] Scarves (3)
- [ ] Stars (2)
- [ ] Sunglasses (3)
- [ ] Sword
- [ ] Ten-gallon hat
- [ ] Ticket
- [ ] Tic-tac-toe
- [ ] Top hat
- [ ] Walking stick

MARATHON-A-SAURUS

FIND THESE ITEMS:

- ☐ Automobile
- ☐ Axe
- ☐ Bird
- ☐ Bowling ball
- ☐ Cactus
- ☐ Cell phone
- ☐ Coffeepot
- ☐ Cup
- ☐ Fire hydrant
- ☐ Fish
- ☐ Jack-o'-lantern
- ☐ Jester's cap
- ☐ Key
- ☐ Kite
- ☐ Lost baseball caps (2)
- ☐ Moustache
- ☐ Pencil
- ☐ Rolling pin
- ☐ Skateboard
- ☐ Socks (2)
- ☐ Star
- ☐ Straw
- ☐ Telescope
- ☐ Tent
- ☐ Traffic light
- ☐ Tulip
- ☐ Turtle
- ☐ Volcano

HARD HAT-A-SAURUS

FIND THESE ITEMS:

- ☐ Arrows (5)
- ☐ Astronaut
- ☐ Balloons (3)
- ☐ Banana peel
- ☐ Bicycle
- ☐ Book
- ☐ Bowling ball
- ☐ Clothes line
- ☐ Comb
- ☐ Cow
- ☐ Fish
- ☐ Fish bowl
- ☐ Football
- ☐ Hearts (2)
- ☐ Igloo
- ☐ Lunchbox
- ☐ Moose head
- ☐ Mouse
- ☐ Paint can
- ☐ Sail
- ☐ Saw
- ☐ Scarf
- ☐ Snake
- ☐ Socks (2)
- ☐ Sunglasses
- ☐ Tepee
- ☐ Thermometer
- ☐ Top hat
- ☐ Turtle
- ☐ Used tire
- ☐ Wheelbarrow

THE FAMOUS STORY OF FRANKENSAURUS

FIND THESE ITEMS:

- ☐ Alarm clock
- ☐ Axe
- ☐ Banana peel
- ☐ Band-aids (2)
- ☐ Baseball bat
- ☐ Baseball cap
- ☐ Bow and arrow
- ☐ Bowling ball
- ☐ Candle
- ☐ Cupcake
- ☐ Dead flower
- ☐ Drum
- ☐ Eyeglasses
- ☐ Fire hydrant
- ☐ Fish
- ☐ Football
- ☐ Heart
- ☐ Knitting needles
- ☐ Lollipop
- ☐ Oil can
- ☐ Paddle
- ☐ Paper airplane
- ☐ Pencils (2)
- ☐ Periscope
- ☐ Pizza
- ☐ Rolling pin
- ☐ Saw
- ☐ Scissors
- ☐ Screwdriver
- ☐ Sunglasses
- ☐ Tape
- ☐ Thermometer
- ☐ Tic-tac-toe
- ☐ Turtle
- ☐ Yo-yo

DINO-WRESTLING
IS REALLY HUGE!

FIND THESE ITEMS:

- ☐ Band-Aid
- ☐ Baseball caps (3)
- ☐ Baseball glove
- ☐ Basketball
- ☐ Bow tie
- ☐ Camera
- ☐ Drinking straw
- ☐ Egg
- ☐ Envelope
- ☐ Flowers
- ☐ Harmonica
- ☐ Headphones (2)
- ☐ Heart
- ☐ Hot dog
- ☐ Ice-cream cone
- ☐ Kite
- ☐ Lost balloons (2)
- ☐ Microphone
- ☐ Necktie
- ☐ Pencils (2)
- ☐ Periscope
- ☐ Scarf
- ☐ Slice of pizza
- ☐ Straw hat
- ☐ Sunglasses
- ☐ Telescope
- ☐ Top hat
- ☐ Yo-yo

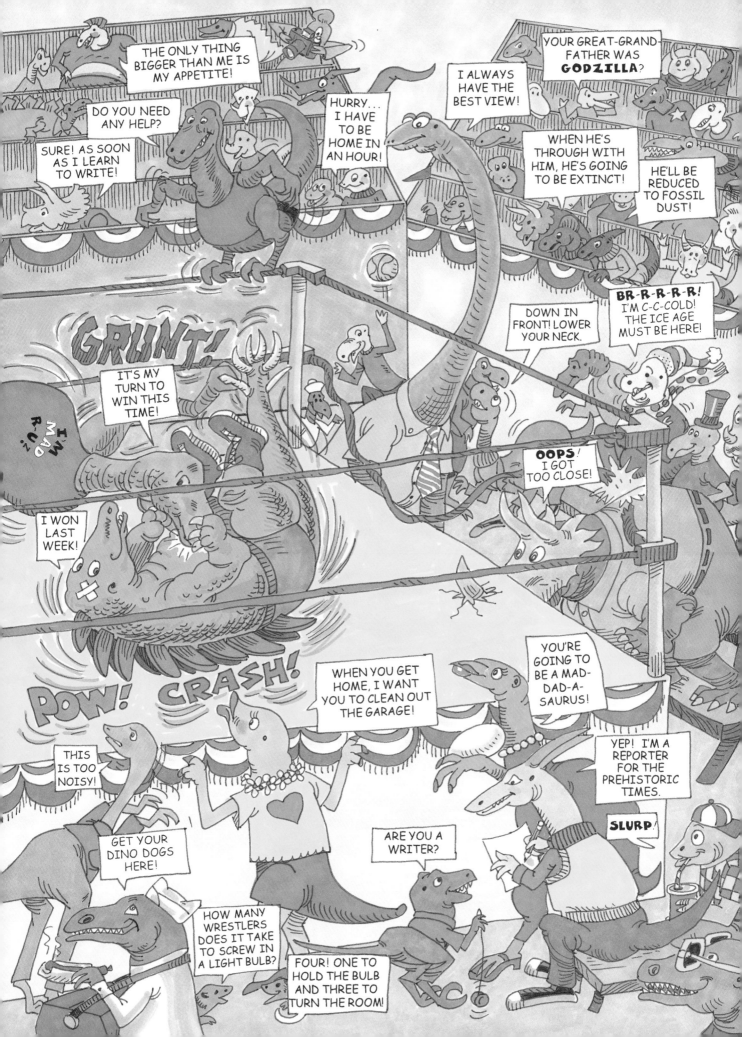

THE VOYAGE OF CHRISTOPHER COLUMBUSAURUS

FIND THESE ITEMS:

- ☐ Balloons (3)
- ☐ Barber pole
- ☐ Bird
- ☐ Brushes (2)
- ☐ Bullhorn
- ☐ Candle
- ☐ Chef's hat
- ☐ Fire hydrant
- ☐ Fishing rod
- ☐ Heart
- ☐ Horseshoe
- ☐ Hourglass
- ☐ Ice-cream cone
- ☐ Key
- ☐ Kite
- ☐ Mermaid
- ☐ Periscope
- ☐ Pie
- ☐ Sock
- ☐ Sunglasses
- ☐ Sailor's cap
- ☐ Telescope
- ☐ Tire
- ☐ Umbrella
- ☐ Yo-yo

DINOSAURS IN SPACE

FIND THESE ITEMS:

- ☐ Apple
- ☐ Banana
- ☐ Band-Aid
- ☐ Barber pole
- ☐ Baseball
- ☐ Baseball cap
- ☐ Bow tie
- ☐ Cane
- ☐ Carrot
- ☐ Coffeepot
- ☐ Cups (2)
- ☐ Envelopes (2)
- ☐ Flower pot
- ☐ Garden hose
- ☐ Hammer
- ☐ Hitchhiker
- ☐ Ice-cream cone
- ☐ Key
- ☐ Kite
- ☐ Lost shoe
- ☐ Medal
- ☐ Oil can
- ☐ Pencil
- ☐ Saw
- ☐ Screwdriver
- ☐ Shovel
- ☐ Speaker
- ☐ Telescope
- ☐ Tepee
- ☐ Tic-tac-toe
- ☐ Toothbrush

DINO VACATIONS IN NEW YORK CITY

FIND THESE ITEMS:

- ☐ Banana
- ☐ Bicycle messenger
- ☐ Bone
- ☐ Burned-out bulbs (3)
- ☐ Camera
- ☐ Cane
- ☐ Clipboard
- ☐ Clothespin
- ☐ Crayon
- ☐ Envelope
- ☐ Fire hydrants (3)
- ☐ Fork
- ☐ Ghost
- ☐ Hearts (2)
- ☐ Horseshoe
- ☐ Ice-cream cone
- ☐ In-line skater
- ☐ Jack-o'-lantern
- ☐ Ladder
- ☐ Lost balloon
- ☐ Mouse
- ☐ Paintbrush
- ☐ Paper airplane
- ☐ Party hat
- ☐ Tepee
- ☐ Worm

DINOSAURS IN KING ARTHUR'S COURT

FIND THESE ITEMS:

- ☐ Balloon
- ☐ Banana
- ☐ Banana peels (2)
- ☐ Baseball cap
- ☐ Basketball
- ☐ Bell
- ☐ Bird
- ☐ Bone
- ☐ Bow tie
- ☐ Candle
- ☐ Carrot
- ☐ Clothespins (3)
- ☐ Earring
- ☐ Feather
- ☐ Ice-cream cone
- ☐ Jestersaurus
- ☐ Jugglesaurus
- ☐ Light bulb
- ☐ Merlinasaurus
- ☐ Pearl necklace
- ☐ Roller skate
- ☐ Sock
- ☐ Swords (3)
- ☐ Telescope
- ☐ Whale

DINO SUPERHEROES

FIND THESE ITEMS:

- [ ] Arrow
- [ ] Banana peel
- [ ] Bone
- [ ] Cactus
- [ ] Chef's hat
- [ ] Drum
- [ ] Envelope
- [ ] Fish
- [ ] Football
- [ ] Gavel
- [ ] Hammer
- [ ] Heart
- [ ] Hot dog
- [ ] Jack-o'-lantern
- [ ] Key
- [ ] Kite
- [ ] Owl
- [ ] Paper airplane
- [ ] Pencil
- [ ] Rabbit
- [ ] Screwdriver
- [ ] Seal
- [ ] Straw
- [ ] Tack
- [ ] Television
- [ ] Toothbrush
- [ ] Umbrella

WILD WEST TOWN

FIND THESE ITEMS:

- [ ] Arrows (2)
- [ ] Axe
- [ ] Badges (2)
- [ ] Balloons (2)
- [ ] Banana
- [ ] Barrel
- [ ] Bones (2)
- [ ] Bow tie
- [ ] Brush
- [ ] Cactus (2)
- [ ] Candle
- [ ] Cheese
- [ ] Coonskin caps (2)
- [ ] Cup
- [ ] Drums (2)
- [ ] Elephant
- [ ] Eyeglasses
- [ ] Fire hydrant
- [ ] Fish
- [ ] Flower
- [ ] Football
- [ ] Heart
- [ ] Horseshoe
- [ ] Pencil
- [ ] Razor
- [ ] Ring
- [ ] Top hat
- [ ] Worm

PICNIC-A-SAURUS

FIND THESE ITEMS:

- ☐ Arrow
- ☐ Baseball caps (2)
- ☐ Bone
- ☐ Cactus
- ☐ Comb
- ☐ Cell phone
- ☐ Eyeglasses (2)
- ☐ Fish
- ☐ Flower
- ☐ Football
- ☐ Forks (3)
- ☐ Four-leaf clover
- ☐ Frog
- ☐ Ghost
- ☐ Hot dog
- ☐ Lamp
- ☐ Lion
- ☐ Lost kite
- ☐ Lost sunglasses
- ☐ Mushroom
- ☐ Pie
- ☐ Pizza delivery dino
- ☐ Propeller
- ☐ Ring
- ☐ Salt shaker
- ☐ Star
- ☐ Yo-yo

A DAY AT

DINO-LAND

FIND THESE ITEMS:

- ☐ Bone
- ☐ Bow tie
- ☐ Fire hydrant
- ☐ Fish
- ☐ Flower
- ☐ Flower pot
- ☐ Football
- ☐ Heart
- ☐ Hot-air balloon
- ☐ Necktie
- ☐ Net
- ☐ Pencil
- ☐ Periscope
- ☐ Pick
- ☐ Pizza delivery dino
- ☐ Plunger
- ☐ Screwdriver
- ☐ Shark fin
- ☐ Shovel
- ☐ Skier
- ☐ Sled
- ☐ Sunglasses
- ☐ Suspenders
- ☐ Tire
- ☐ Turtle

DINO-5... IN CONCERT

FIND THESE ITEMS:

- [ ] Accordion
- [ ] Apple
- [ ] Arrow
- [ ] Astronaut
- [ ] Bandanna
- [ ] Basketball
- [ ] Bell
- [ ] Beret
- [ ] Cane
- [ ] Carrot
- [ ] Crayon
- [ ] Empty birdcage
- [ ] Fish
- [ ] Hearts (3)
- [ ] Key
- [ ] Light bulb
- [ ] Lost balloon
- [ ] Monocle
- [ ] Moon face
- [ ] Moustache
- [ ] Paintbrush
- [ ] Pear
- [ ] Pencil
- [ ] Pizza delivery dino
- [ ] Sailor cap
- [ ] Seal
- [ ] Straw
- [ ] Sunglasses
- [ ] Teapot
- [ ] Thermometer
- [ ] Top hat
- [ ] Whistler

LAST ONE IN IS A
ROTTENSAURUS EGG

FIND THESE ITEMS:

- ☐ Balloons (2)
- ☐ Baseball caps (4)
- ☐ Bird
- ☐ Book
- ☐ Boombox
- ☐ Bone
- ☐ Bowling ball
- ☐ Fire hydrant
- ☐ Flashlight
- ☐ Football
- ☐ Golf club
- ☐ Hammer
- ☐ Horseshoe
- ☐ Ice-cream cone
- ☐ Lamp
- ☐ Mushroom
- ☐ Paper airplane
- ☐ Periscopes (2)
- ☐ Pizza delivery dino
- ☐ Ring
- ☐ Sailor cap
- ☐ Shark fins (2)
- ☐ Starfish
- ☐ Sunglasses (2)
- ☐ Telescope
- ☐ Top hat
- ☐ TV set

SCHOOL-YARDASAURUS

FIND THESE ITEMS:

- ☐ Balloon
- ☐ Banana peel
- ☐ Beret
- ☐ Bones (2)
- ☐ Bow tie
- ☐ Broom
- ☐ Butterfly
- ☐ Camera
- ☐ Coonskin cap
- ☐ Drum
- ☐ Drum major
- ☐ Eyeglasses (2)
- ☐ Fish
- ☐ Heart
- ☐ Hot dog
- ☐ Juggler
- ☐ Kite
- ☐ Lit candle
- ☐ Lollipop
- ☐ Lost cookie
- ☐ Lost sneakers
- ☐ Mailbox
- ☐ Paper airplane
- ☐ Pizza delivery dino
- ☐ Sailor cap
- ☐ Skate
- ☐ Star
- ☐ Sunglasses
- ☐ Tennis racket
- ☐ Tuba
- ☐ Yo-yo

STAND-UP DINO

FIND THESE ITEMS:

- ☐ Airplane
- ☐ Anchor
- ☐ Apple
- ☐ Barrel
- ☐ Baseball bat
- ☐ Binoculars
- ☐ Bone
- ☐ Burned-out bulb
- ☐ Candle
- ☐ Chicken
- ☐ Clothespin
- ☐ Cups (5)
- ☐ Earring
- ☐ Fish (2)
- ☐ Football
- ☐ Heart
- ☐ Hot dog
- ☐ Kite
- ☐ Mailbox
- ☐ Monocle
- ☐ Moustache
- ☐ Pencils (2)
- ☐ Pizza delivery dino
- ☐ Sailboat
- ☐ Sled
- ☐ Sunglasses

MUSEUM-SAURUS

FIND THESE ITEMS:

- ☐ Arrow
- ☐ Astronaut
- ☐ Bib
- ☐ Broom
- ☐ Camera
- ☐ Cane
- ☐ Crack
- ☐ Crown
- ☐ Dart
- ☐ Eyeglasses
- ☐ Fish
- ☐ Flower
- ☐ Golf club
- ☐ Heart
- ☐ Hourglass
- ☐ Menu
- ☐ Moustache
- ☐ Nail
- ☐ Pencils (3)
- ☐ Pizza delivery dino
- ☐ Rock
- ☐ Roll
- ☐ Telescope
- ☐ Toothbrush
- ☐ Top hat
- ☐ Umbrella
- ☐ Volcano
- ☐ Yo-yo

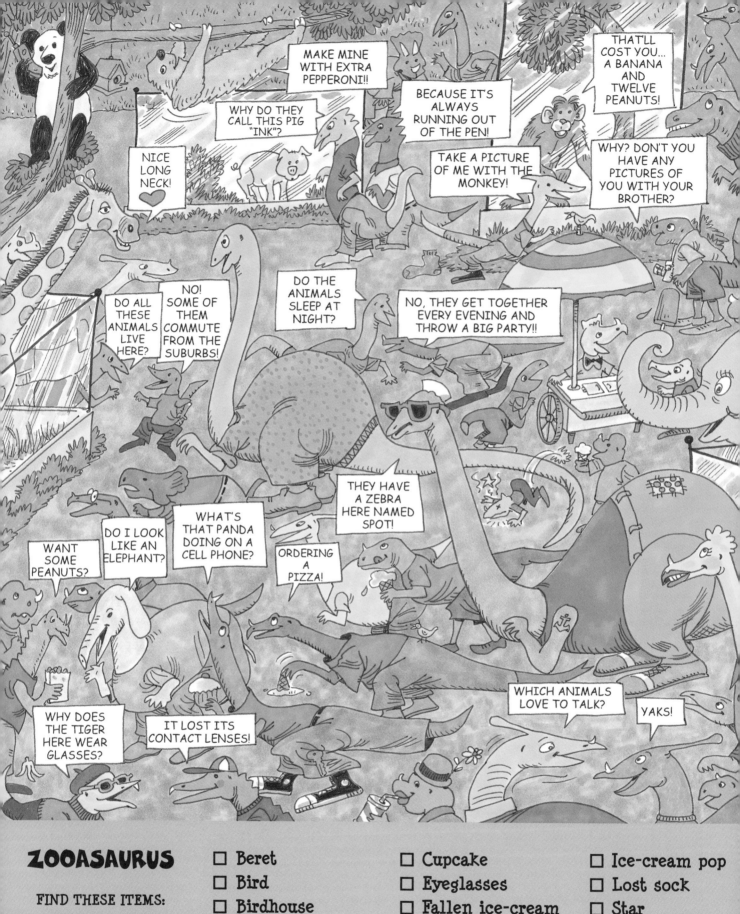

ZOOASAURUS

FIND THESE ITEMS:

- ☐ Anchor tattoo
- ☐ Banana peel
- ☐ Baseball cap
- ☐ Beret
- ☐ Bird
- ☐ Birdhouse
- ☐ Bow tie
- ☐ Camera
- ☐ Cell phone
- ☐ Cupcake
- ☐ Eyeglasses
- ☐ Fallen ice-cream cone
- ☐ Flower
- ☐ Heart
- ☐ Ice-cream pop
- ☐ Lost sock
- ☐ Star
- ☐ Sunglasses (2)

Where's Cupid?

FIND CUPID AMONG THESE CARTOON FAVORITES, AND THESE FUN ITEMS:

- ☐ Balloons (4)
- ☐ Banana peel
- ☐ Baseball
- ☐ Basket
- ☐ Beehive
- ☐ Bone
- ☐ Cactus
- ☐ Candle
- ☐ Cup
- ☐ Feather
- ☐ Flowers (2)
- ☐ Flying bats (2)
- ☐ Hearts (10)
- ☐ Lock
- ☐ Magic lamp
- ☐ Mirror
- ☐ Mushroom
- ☐ Music note
- ☐ Painted egg
- ☐ Piggy bank
- ☐ Pirate
- ☐ Pizzas (2)
- ☐ Tire
- ☐ Top hat
- ☐ Turtle
- ☐ Umbrella

FIND CUPID IN VERONA, AND THESE FUN ITEMS:

- ☐ Baseball cap
- ☐ Bird
- ☐ Bull's-eye
- ☐ Candy cane
- ☐ Duck
- ☐ Fishing pole
- ☐ Football player
- ☐ Frog
- ☐ Hamburger
- ☐ Hot dog
- ☐ Ice skates
- ☐ Key
- ☐ Kites (2)
- ☐ Light bulb
- ☐ Mouse
- ☐ Paper airplane
- ☐ Pie
- ☐ Pillow
- ☐ Propeller
- ☐ Roller skates
- ☐ Saw
- ☐ Skateboard
- ☐ Sock
- ☐ Stars (3)
- ☐ Sunglasses
- ☐ Television

FIND CUPID IN THIS SPOOKY CAVE, AND THESE FUN ITEMS:

- ☐ Balloons (2)
- ☐ Boat
- ☐ Bones (4)
- ☐ Boot
- ☐ Briefcase
- ☐ Broom
- ☐ Candle
- ☐ Dogs (2)
- ☐ Drum
- ☐ Envelope
- ☐ Flowers (3)
- ☐ Football
- ☐ Ghosts (3)
- ☐ Helmets (2)
- ☐ Kite
- ☐ Monsters with horns (4)
- ☐ Mummy
- ☐ Paintbrush
- ☐ Painted eggs (2)
- ☐ Ring
- ☐ Star
- ☐ Sock
- ☐ Turtle
- ☐ Top hat
- ☐ Train engine
- ☐ Umbrella

FIND CUPID AT WASHINGTON'S WEDDING AND THESE FUN ITEMS:

- ☐ Apple
- ☐ Banana peel
- ☐ Bone
- ☐ Bonnet
- ☐ Bowling ball
- ☐ Butterfly
- ☐ Camera
- ☐ Candy cane
- ☐ Chalkboard
- ☐ Crayon
- ☐ Drumstick
- ☐ Egg
- ☐ Feathers (4)
- ☐ Firecracker
- ☐ Fish (2)
- ☐ Hearts (4)
- ☐ Kites (2)
- ☐ Knight
- ☐ Mouse
- ☐ Pizza
- ☐ Rabbits (2)
- ☐ Shovel
- ☐ Snail
- ☐ Socks (3)
- ☐ Surfboard
- ☐ Toaster
- ☐ Umbrella
- ☐ Witch's hats (2)

FIND CUPID IN SHERWOOD FOREST AND THESE FUN ITEMS:

- ☐ Balloon
- ☐ Bell
- ☐ Birdcage
- ☐ Broom
- ☐ Cactus
- ☐ Camel
- ☐ Candle
- ☐ Car
- ☐ Clock
- ☐ Eagle
- ☐ Elephant
- ☐ Feathers (3)
- ☐ Fish (2)
- ☐ Fishing pole
- ☐ Fork
- ☐ Ghosts (2)
- ☐ Gold coin
- ☐ Golf club
- ☐ Humpty Dumpty
- ☐ Igloo
- ☐ Ladder
- ☐ Mice (2)
- ☐ Owl
- ☐ Paintbrush
- ☐ Slingshot
- ☐ Star
- ☐ Sunglasses
- ☐ Turtles (3)

FIND CUPID IN THIS SCENE AND THESE FUN ITEMS:

- ☐ Ant
- ☐ Apple
- ☐ Baseball bat
- ☐ Bears (2)
- ☐ Bone
- ☐ Cat
- ☐ Deer
- ☐ Dog
- ☐ Drum
- ☐ Fish (5)
- ☐ Frog
- ☐ Ghost
- ☐ Guitar
- ☐ Hearts (14)
- ☐ Howling wolf
- ☐ Mouse
- ☐ Pig
- ☐ Porcupine
- ☐ Rabbits (3)
- ☐ Raccoon
- ☐ Skunk
- ☐ Snake in the grass
- ☐ Snake out of the grass
- ☐ Spacecraft
- ☐ Sunflower
- ☐ Windup cowboy

FIND CUPID ON THIS BUSY STREET, AND THESE FUN ITEMS:

- ☐ Banana peel
- ☐ Barrel
- ☐ Basketball hoop
- ☐ Black cat
- ☐ Boat builder
- ☐ Bones (3)
- ☐ Bowling ball
- ☐ Candle
- ☐ Candy cane
- ☐ Chef
- ☐ Firefighter
- ☐ Football player
- ☐ Goat
- ☐ Green wagon
- ☐ Hearts (4)
- ☐ Horses (2)
- ☐ Laundry
- ☐ Music note
- ☐ Newspaper
- ☐ Panda
- ☐ Pole vaulter
- ☐ Red balloon
- ☐ Skateboard
- ☐ Top hat
- ☐ Torch
- ☐ Umbrellas (2)

FIND CUPID IN THE CROCKETT'S YARD, AND THESE FUN ITEMS:

- ☐ Apple
- ☐ Axe
- ☐ Ball
- ☐ Baskets (2)
- ☐ Bears (3)
- ☐ Beaver
- ☐ Bee
- ☐ Bone
- ☐ Broom
- ☐ Candle
- ☐ Chicken
- ☐ Child's wagon
- ☐ Cricket
- ☐ Dogs (2)
- ☐ Goldilocks
- ☐ Hearts (3)
- ☐ Lion
- ☐ Lost hat
- ☐ Moose
- ☐ Pinocchio
- ☐ Rain barrel
- ☐ Rake
- ☐ Shovel
- ☐ Snake
- ☐ Squirrel
- ☐ Tugboat
- ☐ Turkey
- ☐ Wagon wheel

FIND CUPID AMONG THE GRUESOME GHOULIES AND THESE FUN ITEMS:

- ☐ Baseball bat
- ☐ Baseball cap
- ☐ Bird's nest
- ☐ Blue moon
- ☐ Bones (2)
- ☐ Broken TV set
- ☐ Candles (3)
- ☐ Chef's hat
- ☐ Count Dracula
- ☐ Eyeglasses (2)
- ☐ Flowers (3)
- ☐ Ghosts (4)
- ☐ Hearts (4)
- ☐ Hockey stick
- ☐ Jack-o'-lanterns (2)
- ☐ Key
- ☐ Lollipop
- ☐ Mitten
- ☐ Mouse
- ☐ Octopus
- ☐ Piggy bank
- ☐ Pyramid
- ☐ Roller skates
- ☐ Sailor's cap
- ☐ Sled
- ☐ Sock
- ☐ Tent
- ☐ Worms (2)

FIND CUPID ON THIS MOONLIT NIGHT, AND THESE FUN ITEMS:

- ☐ Arrows (2)
- ☐ Axe
- ☐ Bearded man
- ☐ Bell
- ☐ Bone
- ☐ Bowling ball
- ☐ Broken heart
- ☐ Broom
- ☐ Comb
- ☐ Cradle
- ☐ Dog
- ☐ Flying bat
- ☐ Frying pan
- ☐ Hot dog
- ☐ Lost boot
- ☐ Owl
- ☐ Pencil
- ☐ Pie
- ☐ Rabbit
- ☐ Santa Claus
- ☐ Scissors
- ☐ Skateboard
- ☐ Squirrel
- ☐ Telescope
- ☐ Unicorn

FIND CUPID AMONG THE FALLING LEAVES, AND THESE FUN ITEMS:

- ☐ Ball of yarn
- ☐ Balloon
- ☐ Banana peel
- ☐ Bat under a hat
- ☐ Bottle
- ☐ Broken dish
- ☐ Butterfly
- ☐ Cat
- ☐ Crayon
- ☐ Drum
- ☐ Duck
- ☐ Fishing pole
- ☐ Football player
- ☐ Golf ball
- ☐ Goose
- ☐ Hammer
- ☐ Hoe
- ☐ Igloo
- ☐ Key
- ☐ Kite
- ☐ Knife
- ☐ Paper airplane
- ☐ Pigs (2)
- ☐ Pumpkin
- ☐ Rat in a cap
- ☐ Skateboard
- ☐ Umpire

CUPID HAS SHOT
16 ARROWS.

FIND ALL OF
THE ARROWS, AND
THESE FUN ITEMS:

☐ Balloons (2)
☐ Bone
☐ Flowers (12)
☐ Moon face
☐ Mouse
☐ Stars (5)
☐ Wreath